To Alice, Thank you for
your coun   's.
I hope yo
story c

THE CHESSMASTER'S

SECRET

[signature]

THE
CHESSMASTER'S
SECRET

Mary Parker

Matador
9 Priory Business Park,
Wistow Road, Kibworth Beauchamp,
Leicestershire. LE8 0RX
Tel: 0116 279 2299
Email: books@troubador.co.uk
Web: www.troubador.co.uk/matador
Twitter: @matadorbooks

ISBN 978 1789018 264

British Library Cataloguing in Publication Data.
A catalogue record for this book is available from the British Library.

Printed and bound in Great Britain by 4edge Limited
Typeset in 12pt Centaur by Troubador Publishing Ltd, Leicester, UK

Matador is an imprint of Troubador Publishing Ltd

For Bethan, Francesca, Daniel , Petra, Jessica
Lara, Theodore, Sebastian, Makis and Jonty
and remembering Chris

CONTENTS

1

London 1944

THE SHOP OF MECHANICAL MARVELS

IT WAS EASY TO SPOT UNCLE GRIFF ON THE platform at Charing Cross. There was the long raincoat that he always used to wear and the brown hat tilted slightly over one eye. Belle could see his head and shoulders above the swirling steam from the engine as he came down the platform with his stiff-legged walk. He was heading towards them, looking up over the fog and the crowd of passengers and he might have walked right past them but Joe called out 'Hey Uncle Griff, it's us,' and then he stopped right in front of them.

She wanted to run up and hug him as if she was still about six years old. She couldn't trust herself to speak but inside her head she was shouting: 'You are the only one we've got now. Please want us to stay with you.'

'Belle and Joe, by golly,' she heard him say. 'So it is, haven't you both grown? Not much luggage, I see, that's good. Come on then, taxi's waiting.'

She stepped forward and put her arms around his waist pressing her head against the hard material of his raincoat and felt his hand touch her shoulder gently. After all those terrible months she felt safe. Holding his hand tightly she followed Joe out of the station.

London was far worse than she remembered. All she could see from the taxi window was bombed-out houses and craters everywhere. Each pile of rubble looked to her like the remains of their lovely house after the bomb.

As the taxi came near to Trafalgar Square she recognised the church where they'd all sung carols one Christmas. The spire had collapsed and a stone flight of stairs climbed high into emptiness. There was a statue of a little angel with broken wings looking out over the ruins. She felt so choked with sad thoughts that she almost wished she'd never come back to London, and she turned her face to the window so no one would see the tears welling up. Joe was sitting very still and quiet. He was always like that with new people.

'Almost there now,' said her uncle. 'The old shop's just round the corner from the British Museum. It's a bit of a rum place, but there's plenty to do as you'll see.'

'What old shop?' Belle looked a question at Joe but he shrugged back, 'don't know.' Uncle Griff's letter had said something about helping him in a shop for the holidays but with no explanation.

The taxi turned into a narrow street and drew up by a small shop front. Over the window was the green painted sign: *Mechanical Marvels.*

'Welcome,' said Uncle Griff. 'Now here's the surprise.' As he opened the door a bell tinkled and a toy monkey in a red velvet jacket jumped up and down on the table banging a pair of cymbals.

'Hah.' He was smiling and had gone quite pink in the face. 'See I fixed that up myself. There's a wire from the door that triggers the clockwork. Well, what do you think?'

Looking out at them from the shelves were groups of little figures: dancers, clowns, musicians, bears, acrobats, all with their limbs fixed in odd positions as if they had stopped suddenly. The walls of the shop were lined with stacks of cardboard boxes. Old books and catalogues were heaped untidily on top of them. It was difficult to see what else was there as so little light came in through the shop window, almost black with London grime. Belle wrinkled her nose at the smell of dust and mouse droppings. What a mess!

'It all needs a bit of a clean-up of course,' said Uncle Griff, 'and we'll have to sort out these boxes, but there are some amazing things here. Look at this one!'

He showed off the characters one by one – a drummer boy, a ballerina, an Indian snake charmer. 'They all needed a bit of work,' he said, turning the key on the drummer boy. 'This little fellow was a beast of a fiddly job, but just look at him go now!' The little drummer's sticks beat a rat-a-tat-tat and they heard the trumpeter join in from the

3

other side of the shop although Belle hadn't noticed Uncle Griff winding that one up.

Joe was still quiet but he'd hardly taken his eyes off the shelves since they'd come into the shop. 'Does this one work, Uncle Griff?' He held up a character in red tights and a spangled coat. Two small red horns poked out from under his round black hat and a long tail was draped over one arm.

'Mephisto, the old devil?' said Uncle Griff, 'Yes indeed.'

When Joe turned the key, Mephisto rolled his eyes, turned his head towards Belle and gave a jaunty wave of his hand before bowing very low. Uncle Griff laughed, 'The old devil pays his respects to you, young lady. Come on, there are plenty more to try.'

Belle couldn't wait to have a go. Nobody talked much. They moved from one mechanical marvel to the next, turning keys and pushing levers to start the clockwork. There was a clash of cymbals, the sound of flutes and drums and tinkling music boxes. The figures were jumping, dancing, bowing and playing instruments. Right at the back a silver swan dipped its long neck to pick up a fish. It was beautiful.

Uncle Griff laughed – a sudden loud burst, which made Belle want to laugh back. The tightness in her chest which had been there since the train pulled into the station began to ease off. Then one by one the mechanisms wound down and the characters grew still. The silence seemed strange and she felt some of the awkwardness come back.

'Right,' said Uncle Griff, abruptly breaking the silence. 'There's a small room upstairs, but the rooms out at the back haven't been sorted out yet. I hope you two don't mind sharing.'

'No, we don't mind,' said Belle, 'Come on Joe, what's up?'

Joe was still staring at the characters on the shelves with that faraway look she knew well. His blue eyes had become dark discs. Nothing shone out of them, everything had gone deep inside. He spoke softly to her. 'They were looking at me. I'm sure they were. The clockwork's run down but they're still alive. I could feel them staring at my back and when I turned round. Old Meffy what's-his-name, the old devil, was looking straight at me.'

Belle knew what to do when Joe was like this. She put her arms round her brother and whispered in his ear. 'Joe come on, we're at Uncle Griff's shop. They're just mechanical toys, they're not alive.'

But he looked straight at her with those strange blank eyes. 'You don't see them, Belle. They're magic. I know they are. They're wonderful.'

Belle took a quick look at the characters again. The old devil's face with its straggly beard was turned towards her and his eyes did look bright, almost real. But Joe's always imagining things. I'll just have to explain to Uncle Griff. I hope he doesn't think he's crazy.

'Joe has some unusual ideas sometimes,' she mumbled.

But Uncle Griff didn't seem at all surprised and just smiled at Joe. 'Unusual ideas, old chap? You must be a bit like me then. When I had polio in India I had to stay in a dark room for weeks and I used to talk to all sorts of extraordinary creatures. They were truly magnificent.' He picked up the drummer boy again. 'These little fellows haven't talked to me yet, but I hope they will one day.'

Belle stared at her uncle. Does he really mean that, or is he just trying to make Joe feel OK? He was stooped over the table, tinkering with one of the mechanical figures again, looking for all the world as if no one had said anything odd at all. He turned round as Joe yawned loudly.

'Right,' he said, 'It's late, let's get you settled, plenty to do tomorrow.' Picking up their bags he headed for the stairs.

Belle loved their little room right from the start. It felt like home. There were two mattresses on the floor, both covered with brightly coloured rugs. There was just space for a small table under the window and a wooden stool by one of the beds. Yet more old boxes were stacked up all around the walls.

Joe threw himself onto the bed. 'This shop's amazing,' he said. 'There's magic here. I could feel it everywhere.'

Belle shook her head. 'Well, Uncle Griff seems to know what you're talking about. It's a wonderful, crazy shop and I just love all those mechanical marvels, but I don't know what you mean about the magic.'

'Oh, but I hope you will feel it. I think you must.' Joe grabbed hold of her hand. 'I can't ever explain magic to other people, but really it's great... it's like having doors that open into other worlds, where everything's different. Do you understand?'

What's he trying to tell me? Is all this magic stuff just in his head, or does he mean that he actually visits other worlds? Belle's head felt too heavy with tiredness to work it out.

'No, I don't understand about magic, but I'll try, really I will. This shop's just the right place for it.' She put her arms out and hugged him. His closeness and his warm musty smell made her feel comfortable and sleepy. 'Just promise me one thing,' she whispered, 'if you ever disappear into one of your funny worlds... that you'll always, always come back.'

2

THE STRANGE
MR KEMPEL

THE CLOCK STRIKING EIGHT WOKE BELLE THE
next morning and for a moment she couldn't remember
where she was. Then she saw Joe sitting cross-legged on his
mattress sorting out the contents of one of the boxes, with a
tin of brightly coloured children's bricks spread across his bed.

'Look, Belle, I found a chessboard and I'm just looking
for the men. Ah, here they are.' He opened a carved wooden
box and tipped a set of white and red chess pieces onto the
sheets. 'Great! Perhaps I can play with Uncle Griff.'

'Where did all those boxes come from?'

Joe was moving round the room looking at one after
another. 'They must have been posted to the shop. This
one's got foreign stamps.' The box he was unpacking still
had some of the brown paper attached, with an address
written in large handwriting. *To Gerald Duport, Antique Toys
and Automata, Bloomsbury, London.*

'Who's he?' asked Joe. 'By the way, how did Uncle Griff get this shop? I mean did he buy it or did he collect all those mechanical marvels himself?'

From downstairs Belle could hear the rattling of plates and there was a good smell of toast.

'I don't know. Why don't you ask him at breakfast? Come on, we'd better get down there?'

Uncle Griff was pouring out tea. His hair was tousled and he was wearing a dressing gown that looked as if it belonged to an Indian Maharaja. His answer to Joe's question about the shop came as a surprise to both of them.

'Believe it or not old chap, I won it.'

Joe's mouth dropped open. 'Won it? What, like in a raffle or something?'

'No, I won it in a game of cards from an old mate of mine, a Frenchman called Gerard Duport. He loved these little mechanical figures and he travelled around Europe hunting for them. Then he had them shipped back to London and he bought this place here. He was going to run it himself one day, but he went off to Philadelphia and of course the war came and he never made it back.'

'So is he in Philadelphia now?' asked Joe.

'No,' Uncle Griff shook his head. 'I'm sorry to say the old chap's dead.'

'But how did you get the shop?'

'Well, as I said, I won it from him on a hand of poker, some years ago. Old Duport had no cash and he offered to play me for the shop. I won the game, but I didn't take the bet seriously and then one day I got a registered letter with the deeds of this place and a note from some lawyers dealing with Duport's will telling me that the shop and its contents was mine.'

'So it really is all yours,' said Joe. 'Gosh, what treasure!'

'It's a bit of all right, isn't it?' agreed Uncle Griff. 'The trouble is, I don't know if I can afford to keep it. There are rates to be paid on the shop, you see. The roof's leaking and there's a lot of repair work to be done. I reckon the bomb that hit the end of this street must have shaken the foundations and you can see all the cracks in the walls. It'll take quite a bit of money to set it right and I'm a bit short of the old spondulix.'

Joe's face was a picture of amazed admiration. Belle felt a bubble of laughter rising up. Winning a shop? What a crazy story! Uncle Griff isn't really like a grown up at all.

'If you need to make money, Uncle Griff, you're going to have to sell some of these mechanical marvels,' she said. 'But nobody's going to come and buy anything while the shop looks like this. We'd better get started, hadn't we?'

All that day they worked at cleaning and tidying the shop, washing the grimy windows and shelves, sweeping piles of dirt and mouse droppings from the floor and re-arranging the boxes of toys. By late afternoon it already looked less like a dump and more like a shop, and Uncle Griff stood in the doorway with mugs of tea.

'By Jove, What a transformation! You two are quite a team.'

Gradually over the next few days they put all the shelves in order. Most mornings Uncle Griff sat at his table mending the broken figures, and sometimes someone would drop in for a chat or a passer-by would drift in out of curiosity, but so far there had been no customers. Belle began to understand the problem of bringing money into the shop.

But there was one man who Belle and Joe noticed from time to time looking in the shop window. He was tall and wore a long grey overcoat and high black boots. Joe said he'd seen him more than once, standing very still at the corner of the shop.

'He sort of looks in sideways through the glass,' he told Belle, 'as if he's trying to see what's going on inside. Perhaps we should ask Uncle Griff if he knows him.'

The next afternoon, when Belle was on her way back from the shops, she saw him there again. He gave a little bow, rather formal and old fashioned, and she moved back as she felt an odd cold shiver. What is it about him? Is he dangerous? A spy perhaps? We've been told to look out for spies in wartime, but for Heaven's sake, who'd spy on a toy shop?

The man nodded briefly to her, then turned and walked away.

'Perhaps he doesn't think we're open for customers yet,' she said to Joe. 'Next time we see him I think we should ask him in. He might buy something.'

But they didn't have to ask him because the next morning he rang the bell himself. Joe opened the door as the monkey jumped up and down, banging his cymbals.

'Ah,' she heard the stranger say. 'The musical monkey, delightful.'

At the same time Belle distinctly heard a rustle of movement from the shelves as if the mechanical figures were shifting their positions, but she knew that nobody had wound them up that morning.

She wanted to be polite because this man was actually her first customer, but something about him still made her uncomfortable. His face reminded her of statues in the museum, pale and cold. Thin wisps of hair straggled down to the collar of his old-fashioned coat and there was a smell of damp clothes which made her think he might be sleeping rough, although he didn't look like a tramp.

'Good morning,' she said. 'Would you like to see more of the collection? Our uncle, who owns the shop, is out but we can show you some of the mechanical figures if you'd like.'

But the strange man didn't answer. He seemed too busy, scanning the shelves intensely, looking for something.

'We have more boxes upstairs...' said Belle.

'Do you know anything of a chess-playing automaton?' the man interrupted. 'It is known as the Turk.'

'We've catalogued everything we've unpacked so far,' said Belle, 'but we haven't found a chess-playing automaton. When was it made?'

The man gave an odd smile, as if she should already know the answer.

'It was made in 1770 by Baron von Kempelen and presented at the court of the Empress Maria Theresa in

Vienna. It has been lost for many years, but I believe it to have a connection with your shop.'

Then he clicked the heels of his black boots together and gave another little bow.

'My apologies, young lady, for disturbing you and your brother. My name is Kempel. I will call again, if I may, in case you find anything to help me in my search.' With that he left.

Joe stared after him. 'Gosh, what a weird customer. What do you think he wants?' He turned to the shelves. 'He brought some strange vibrations with him. These little characters seemed all worked up when he came in.'

Belle had been waiting to tell her brother. 'I felt the magic this time,' she said, 'I really did. I could hear the figures moving all by themselves, as if they were worried or excited or something.'

'I knew you would,' said Joe. 'There's so much magic here and I reckon Uncle Griff feels it too. Perhaps he knows something about that strange old man and the mechanical chess player.'

'No, I don't know a Mr Kempel,' said Uncle Griff when they asked him that evening. 'What does he look like?' Belle gave a description of the long grey overcoat and high black boots. 'He's got a foreign accent.' she said.

Uncle Griff shook his head. 'I've never come across him, but I do know about the Turk. It was a famous automaton in its time; a life-sized model dressed in a Turkish costume, who sat behind a cabinet and played some of the most important people in Europe — and what's more it usually beat them. It toured all the capital cities of Europe and was a top-hole attraction. Everyone wanted to see it. Hang on a minute! I saw a picture of it somewhere in one of Gerald's old magazines.'

He flipped through the pages.

'Ah here it is.' He handed the magazine over to Belle. There was a picture of a man wearing splendid fur trimmed robes and a turban. He was reaching out to make a move on the chessboard in front of him.

'Wow, he looks very real,' said Joe. 'What was he made of?'

'The head was carved out of wood. I think the eyes would have been glass and it looks as if they added some dark hair for that dashing moustache. Would you have fancied a game with him Joe? He was a mighty good player it seems.'

'But how did a clockwork model work out all the chess moves? That wasn't possible all those years ago, was it?' said Belle.

Uncle Griff shook his head, 'I don't see how it could have been.'

'Is it possible now?' asked Joe.

'Well, that's a really interesting question. From what I hear it could be possible soon,' said Uncle Griff. 'A chum of mine told me about some new machines, computers. She won't tell me what they're working on because it's all top secret, of course. But I reckon they might be trying to crack the enemy codes. A machine like that might be able to play chess one day.'

'So how did the Turkish automaton win all those games against famous men?' For some reason Belle felt that she just had to know.

Uncle Griff shrugged. 'Well it must have been a hoax, I'd say, but the secret was well kept and I don't think anyone knows exactly how they did it. Hey, talking about chess, I need to take revenge for my defeat. Where's the board?'

Joe laughed as he set up the chessmen. He had beaten his uncle in only fifteen moves the day before.

3

THE TURKISH
CHESSMASTER APPEARS

IN THE MIDDLE OF THE NIGHT BELLE WOKE
suddenly and saw Joe sitting bolt upright in his bed.

Nightmares, she thought and leaned over. 'Joe are you OK?'

No answer from Joe. She could just make out his face
in the sliver of moonlight from under the blackout curtain.
His eyes were tight shut but she thought she saw his lips
moving. He turned his head as if to speak to her. 'White's
move,' he said.

Belle laughed, 'Joe, Joe it's me. You're dreaming. Who
are you playing chess with?'

Joe was awake now. He rubbed his eyes, shaking his head
from side to side. 'It's the Turk, the Turkish chessmaster.'

'What, the one in the magazine?'

'No, no, a real person, like the picture in the magazine,
the turban and the silky robes and everything, but he's
much younger and he's not carved out of wood.'

'Tell me more,' whispered Belle.

Joe's voice was thick with sleep. 'It's a foreign country; we're playing chess under a tree. There's blue sky and the sun's really hot and people are walking about in long robes, selling fruit and stuff.'

'But what about the Turkish chessmaster?'

'He's a brilliant player,' Joe paused. 'But there's something wrong. I think he wants me to do something really important for him, but I don't know what.'

'Is it more than just a dream? Do you think your chess player's trying to tell you something about finding the automaton?'

'I don't know, Belle, perhaps,' Joe answered dreamily. His head flopped back onto the pillow and she saw that his eyes were closed again. She pulled his blankets over him and snuggled back down in her own bed, but her mind was still busy.

The Turkish chessmaster must still be around somewhere, is that what Joe's dream was about? Perhaps Uncle Griff's old friend, Gerald, knew about it.

Her head began to feel fuzzy with sleep, the pillow was soft and comfortable and she knew nothing more until she woke in the early morning.

Joe's bed was empty. Where is he? Pulling on her dressing gown she ran downstairs but hesitated on the bottom step. Something's different. Instead of the usual dusty old smell of the shop, the room had a sweet spicy scent and the air felt heavy and warm.

A sound like whispering voices made her turn to the mechanical figures on the shelves. It was a restless, anxious sound, as if something had disturbed them and they were signalling to each other. The ballet dancer was finishing a pirouette and raised her finger to her lips, warning Belle to be quiet, while the little Japanese lady silently pointed with her fan towards the front of the shop.

Silhouetted against the light from the shop window was a man playing chess with her brother. Although the face was in shadow, she knew him instantly as the Turkish chessmaster from the magazine. He wore the same splendid turban and robes and was sitting behind a large wooden cabinet, just like the picture.

'Joe,' she hissed, 'Joe!'

He seemed not to hear her, totally absorbed in the game with his strange partner. From the way his shoulders were hunched in concentration she guessed he was playing a difficult move. As the ghostly chess player leant across the board she caught a glimpse of his face under the turban; young and good looking with very dark, sparkling eyes, certainly not the carved face of the automaton.

There seemed to be a pause in the game, which was broken by a sudden burst of laughter. Then a strange sound came from inside the cabinet, a mechanical voice, croaking out a word she didn't recognise. It sounded like 'Échec, Échec', and she saw Joe's shoulders slump in defeat.

She hardly had time to realise that the game was over, and that check mate had been called, before she felt a fierce draft of air rush through the room. The outline of the chess player fluttered lightly like a paper cut-out and without a sound both he and the cabinet disappeared.

'Joe? Joe! What's going on?'

He turned round. His cheeks were flushed, his sleep-tousled hair sticking up in tufts and his eyes took a few seconds to focus on her, but he didn't answer her question. He just sat there shaking his head gently from side to side.

'That move into check mate. I've never come across it before. I just didn't see it coming.'

Belle felt a rush of irritation.

'Don't just sit their shaking your head like a stupid old donkey. I want to know what's going on.'

He looked up at her in surprise as if he was just waking up.

'I don't know... I'm sorry... I really don't know.'

'Is he the chess player from your dream?'

Joe was blinking his eyes and he looked around as if still working out where he was. 'Did you see him too?'

Belle nodded.

'When I woke up this morning I came down here to set up the board because I wanted to work out a new opening move and I was just looking at the board and thinking about it when I felt that there was someone on the other side of the table I thought it was Uncle Griff so I said something to him but he didn't answer. When I looked up it was my Turkish chess player. I just stared at him and he smiled at me and reached out his arm and made the opening move.'

The sound of the monkey's cymbals made them both jump.

'Someone at the door?' whispered Joe, 'Who'd come to the shop so early? We're not even open yet.'

Through the glass Belle could see the tall figure of Mr Kempel on the doorstep and felt her stomach tighten in an instinctive warning. What does he want? But before she could go to the door she found that he was already in the room.

He looked different from last time, much less composed, and he'd been hurrying to get here. His thin hair was ruffled and a light film of sweat shone on his pale skin. He clicked his heels and bowed with his usual formal politeness.

How did he walk straight into the shop? The door's still locked isn't it? Who is he, anyway? Belle decided not to tell him anything until they knew more about him.

'Good morning, Mr Kempel. We have been looking for information about the Turkish chessmaster, as you asked, but I'm sorry to say we haven't come up with anything yet.'

He waved his bony hand at her as if he wasn't listening and moved past her into the shop. A flicker of excitement crossed his face when he saw Joe by the chessboard. He already knows about the Turk's visit, thought Belle.

Bending down he looked straight at the boy. His voice was tense but friendly.

'You have seen him, haven't you? You have seen my chessmaster?'

When Joe gave a little nod, he continued as if talking to himself.

'I knew he must be here. That is the reason I was drawn to this funny little shop. But why here? Why?'

For a few moments he stood staring at the chessboard.

'You understand, don't you, that it is very important to me that I find him. May I sit down for a moment?'

He took a handkerchief out of his pocket to mop his face and Belle noticed how thin his arm was. His coat sleeve seemed almost empty. His hands were shaking and he looked as if he might collapse. She hurried to get him a chair.

'Thank you, my dear young lady,' he said, as he sat down, and for the first time he looked directly up at her. But the eyes that searched her face were not like an old man's eyes. They were clear and dark, almost black, and they looked straight at her. She turned her head quickly so as not to show her surprise.

'Ah,' he said softly, 'so now you know that I am not as I seem. Will you tell me what happened this morning? I assure you that my search is an honest one and will bring no harm to you or your brother.'

As she hesitated she felt Joe push past her to tell his story.

'It's the Turkish chessmaster. I played chess with him, at first only in a dream and then, this morning, he was here in the shop. He's an amazing player.'

Mr Kempel nodded his head. 'Ah yes, he is indeed.'

Joe was rushing on. 'We found the picture in a magazine so we know what the Turkish chessmaster looks like, and he wears the same clothes and everything, but this isn't a wooden model. He's a real person.' Joe hesitated and looked carefully at Mr Kempel. 'Or perhaps he's the spirit of a real person. Could that be it?'

Mr Kempel looked approvingly at the boy. 'You understand such things, don't you? Perhaps it was not by accident that I found you here. Yes, you are right. You have been playing chess with the spirit of a young Turk who lived many years ago in the Ottoman court. His name is Kadir. I have been searching for him for a long time but he will not come to me.'

With a grunt of pain, he raised his old body out of the chair. 'I am sure that you can help me and I request you please, if you see him again, to contact me. Here is my card with my address in London... and here...' He drew a purse from his coat pocket and took out a handful of pound notes.

'This is for you and your sister to thank you for helping me in my search.'

Then with a click of his heels and a bow Mr Kempel turned and walked slowly out of the shop.

4

SEARCHING FOR THE CHESSMASTER

As the shop door closed behind Mr Kempel, Belle and Joe stared at each other.

Belle felt as if she had been picked up and shaken. She plonked herself down on the chair.

'Who is he, Joe? He's so strange. Did you notice his eyes?'

Joe seemed deep in thought. 'I think he's travelling,' he said suddenly.

'What? You mean travelling from country to country? That's difficult in wartime, you know.'

'No I mean travelling in time. I've been trying to work out what's different about him and I think that he could be from another time… you know, an earlier time.'

'From an earlier time? You mean he isn't alive anymore? Is he a ghost?'

Just as she said it, Belle felt certain that this was true; the chill he always brought with him and the smell of damp, his pale face and the eyes that looked so unnaturally young. And that comment of his: *'Ah now you know that I am not as I seem.'* He'd appeared in the shop that morning without even opening the door. Her mind raced on...

'You're right Joe. All that heel-clicking and the funny little bows that he does, I just thought it was because he's foreign, but he's from the olden days, isn't he?'

Joe nodded. 'That's what I think. Something to do with his search for the Turkish chessmaster has brought him into our time and to the shop. I reckon we should help him find it, don't you? Perhaps the original model is somewhere right here in London. Uncle Griff said it toured the capital cities of Europe. It might be stored somewhere and perhaps people have forgotten about it.'

'We've got the names of all the London dealers from the magazines,' Belle agreed. 'We could look them up.'

She pointed to the pile of pound notes in Joe's lap. 'Look at all that money he's given us already. He would pay much more than that if we actually found the chessmaster for him. We really need the money and we can tell Uncle Griff that we're helping Mr Kempel with his search.'

But at tea time, when they told their uncle about Mr Kempel's second visit, his reply wasn't what they'd expected.

'I'm afraid it's a hopeless search,' he said. 'I'm surprised Mr Kempel doesn't know. The automaton was destroyed by fire in a museum in Philadelphia in about 1850.'

'Oh, no!' Disappointment swept over Belle. Into her mind came a picture of flames flickering round the carved wooden face, the robes already on fire.

Joe looked puzzled. 'But if that fire was all those years ago, how come you still know all about it?'

'There are the diaries and letters from the people who watched him play chess at the exhibitions around Europe. The Turk was brought to London, you know. People were fascinated and some of them claimed to have solved the mystery of how the whole thing worked. But I'm afraid the old mechanical chessmaster is no more. Burnt to a cinder, I believe. I think you'd better tell your Mr Kempel to call off his search.'

He smiled at their sad faces. 'Hey, but if you're really interested, there's plenty more you can find out for him. We've got piles of those old automata magazines from Gerard. You could find out what happened in the fire and so on and write it all up. I'm sure your old fellow would be pleased with that, wouldn't he?'

Next day Belle and Joe were sitting at the work table in the shop with back copies of *Automata and Mechanical Toys* spread out in front of them. Joe cut out anything Belle found about the Turkish chessmaster and pasted it into an exercise book.

'Oh, here's another one for the book,' she called out. 'The Mechanical Chess-Playing Turk...' she stopped reading. 'Gosh, I don't believe it. Joe, come and look at this.'

'What?' He rushed to look over her shoulder. There, looking out at them from the magazine, was the face of their visitor. A younger man, but it was unmistakably Mr Kempel. Belle read out: *A portrait of Baron Wolfgang von Kempelen, the inventor of the famous mechanical chess player known as the Turk, which was constructed in the late 18th century and presented at the court of Empress Maria Theresa of Austria.*

'So that's it! Mr Kempel is Baron somebody and the chess player is his own invention! You were absolutely right, Joe. He is a time traveller. But what's he looking for now? Surely he must know about the fire in the museum, or do you think the chessmaster might have survived somehow?'

'I don't think it's the mechanical chess player he's after at all,' said Joe. 'I think it's the young Turk from my dreams, the one he calls Kadir. He said that he'd been searching for him for a long time.'

'He must be hoping that the spirit will come back to play chess with you again. I reckon we'll have another visit from Mr Kempel soon, and we've got lots to ask him about when he comes.'

But the days passed and there was no sign of him. Belle kept looking at the door expecting to see the tall figure appear. She really hoped he would come. She had rehearsed his name in her mind, 'Baron von Kempelen', so that she would say it correctly and had thought of all the questions she wanted to ask. Imagine someone actually having been at the court of Empress Maria Theresa! Joe's dreams about playing chess with the young Turk seemed to have stopped as well, and even the mechanical figures on the shelves had gone quiet.

Perhaps our adventure's over, thought Belle, but there was something more important on her mind. She'd been ticking off the days on the calendar in the kitchen. The Easter holidays were nearly over and Uncle Griff had said nothing about any plans for them. Will he let us stay on here? We all seem to be getting on fine and I know we're useful in the shop. Surely he's not going to send us back, is he? She didn't want to upset Joe so she said nothing about it but as the date drew nearer, she grew more and more worried.

5

THE END OF THE HOLIDAYS

THE BLOW FELL THE NEXT MORNING AT breakfast as she and Joe were about to clear the table.

'By the way,' said Uncle Griff. 'I meant to ask you. When do your holidays end?'

Belle saw Joe's face crumble. He looked hard at the floor and his brown fringe flopped over his face.

'I don't want to go back,' he muttered. 'I don't want to go back ever.'

Uncle Griff seemed taken by surprise. 'But I thought you were having a jolly time down there with all your chums, and what about your school and all that?'

Joe's bottom lip trembled. 'I haven't got any chums. There's only Belle. The boys at Benions don't like me because I can't help in the fields with my asthma and they call me a sissy because I'm scared of that smelly old bull. And I hate school. I'm rubbish at reading and it's boring.

Please don't send me back, Uncle Griff. I want to stay here.'

Uncle Griff glanced at Belle, then turned away. He looked uncomfortable and was fiddling with the pen in his top pocket. Belle found herself trembling. The thought of going back made her feel sick. Uncle Griff doesn't want Joe to be upset, I can see that, but he's trying not to look at either of us. I'm pretty sure that's because he doesn't want us to stay on.

'Well, well,' he said, 'that's a turn up for the books. I'm a bit flummoxed now. What to do?'

He turned to Belle again, as if hoping that she would help. But Belle took one look at Joe's stricken face and made up her mind. I'm not going to let Joe go back to the Benions, whatever Uncle Griff thinks. I don't care whether he wants to keep us here or not.

She had to tell him, even if it meant talking about things that she tried not to think about. She felt her voice wobbling.

'It wasn't jolly, Uncle Griff, it wasn't jolly at all. We were just packed off you see, with all the other evacuees. There were lots of other children at the station, but we didn't even know where we were going. We were the only ones sent to Pendleton Green and there wasn't anyone to meet us. There were these people, the Benions, who had a farm there. They were supposed to take in evacuee children, but they only wanted them to work on the farm. They were really horrible to Joe.' She reached her hands up to her face, tears were welling up. 'I tried to look after him, but...' she could hardly go on. 'We can't go back,' she whispered, 'we just can't.'

She looked up. Uncle Griff's face had gone rather red and he was blowing his nose loudly. Is he crying? Grown-ups don't cry do they? For a few moments he said nothing at all, he just sat there looking down at his feet. Then he put up one hand, drawing it across his forehead and rubbing his eyes. He reached over to put his arms around Joe's shoulders. 'I'm sorry, old chap,' he said softly. 'I didn't know. It's the money you see. I don't know how we can keep the shop going. But don't worry; you're not going back there. I had no idea... damned farmers! No, we'll manage somehow.' He gave a shrug of his shoulders, almost talking to himself. 'What the heck? There'll be changes coming soon anyway. Surely this blooming war can't last forever.'

Relief swept over Belle as she saw Joe's face explode with delight. Oh, thank goodness. But she felt completely drained as if she'd just run a mile uphill and her worries quickly came rushing back. What about the money? We haven't got any and what'll happen to us if Uncle Griff has to sell the shop? But when Joe jumped down from his chair and flung his arms around his uncle she just felt a glow of happiness. She gave him a smile which was still a bit shaky.

'There's a school just down the road that Joe could go to, and I can give him a hand with his schoolwork. He's really clever, it's just that he finds the reading hard and the teacher was always picking on him.'

Uncle Griff nodded and gave Joe a little pat on the back. Then in his jokey-uncle voice he said: 'Righto, that's agreed, eh? I've just taken in two young refugees from Kent. I must be bonkers! Come on, we can't sit here all day, there's work to be done.'

For the rest of the holidays Belle and Joe worked hard in the shop and made it much smarter than before, with a fine brass lamp hanging from the ceiling, a dark red Eastern rug on the floor and a handsome leather-topped desk to replace the old rickety table. They had rescued the furniture, together with a tea set and some other useful items, from one of the rummage sales which were held in the bombed-out streets nearby. The rug had a burn in one corner which was neatly covered by a chair and the desk had one new, and not quite matching, leg. But it looked good.

'Just the ticket,' Uncle Griff said. 'That'll bring in the customers. You'll see.'

But sadly it didn't bring customers in and Belle was worried again. She knew that there wasn't much money left. She'd seen a bill, with FINAL NOTICE written in red, lying on Uncle Griff's desk and they were having to share out food more carefully at meal times.

'If only we could find a way of making some money ourselves,' she said to Joe as they lay in bed at night. 'There must be something we can do.'

His sleepy voice came back. 'Don't worry, Belle. I'm sure it's going to be all right. I can just feel it. We're not going back to the stinky Benions ever, that's all I care about.

I love this shop...' There was a pause and she thought he must have dropped off. '...and Uncle Griff.'

'Yes... so do I,' she whispered back as she snuggled down into her pillows.

6

THE TURK AND
MR KEMPEL AGAIN

SHE WAS WOKEN BY SOMEONE PULLING ON HER
pillow. Sleepily she tried to push him away, but then realised
that it was Joe trying to tell her something.

'Belle, Belle, I played chess in my dream again, it was just
like before, with the palm trees and the sunshine and everything.'

Belle was wide awake now and listening. 'With the
same young Turk, the spirit?'

'Yes. It was definitely him, but we didn't finish the
game. I don't know why. He wasn't winning quite as easily
as before and then I think he was called back somewhere.
He disappeared suddenly.'

Joe was sitting on the edge of her mattress and Belle
saw that he already had his dressing gown on.

'The thing is, my chessboard's downstairs, and I just
had a funny sort of feeling that he might come back to
finish the game. Will you come down with me?'

Belle didn't need to be asked twice. She was dying to see the chess player again.

As they got to the bottom of the stairs they stopped and Joe wrinkled his nose.

'What's that smell?' he whispered.

Belle breathed in the sweet muskiness. 'Oh yes, it's just the same as last time – and listen!' Sure enough, from the shelves came the tinkling sound of the mechanical figures moving and signalling to each other. The drummer boy gave a roll on his drum as if to announce an important event.

'I think he's here,' she said, but Joe had already dashed into the room.

She saw the figure of the Turk in all his finery bow to greet Joe, and at the same time the sound of the monkey's cymbals at the door made her turn round.

In that moment the chess player reached out his arm and swept the chessmen tumbling to the ground. There was the sound of softly blowing wind and he was gone.

They both knew what to expect. Mr Kempel in his long grey coat was already standing in the shop. He paused briefly by the shelves, bowed politely to Mephisto, who responded with a deep bow and a sweep of his hand, and then moved across the room towards the chessboard. 'He was here again wasn't he?'

Joe pointed to the scattered chessmen. 'Yes, just now. He knocked all the chessmen off the board.'

Mr Kempel didn't look surprised, 'Ah yes, he has done that before. He is well known for his temper. It seems he does not want to meet me.' Then, almost to himself, 'But why does he come here?' He shook his head as if he had no answer to his own question and appeared lost in thought for a few minutes.

'Good morning, Mr Kempel,' Belle said politely. The old man turned round slowly and gave his usual polite bow. 'Good morning, young lady. I apologise for not greeting you before. I had not realised you were here.'

'Would you like to sit down?' she said, moving a chair towards him. 'I will make a cup of tea if you like. There's something we want to ask you about.'

'I will sit down if I may, but no tea thank you.' He looked straight at her. 'So, what is it that you want to know?'

Joe joined them. 'Well the thing is, we know who you really are,' he said quietly.

The dark eyes didn't flicker. 'Ah that was clever of you, but you are unusual children. You know then that I am Baron von Kempelen, and the mechanical chess player was one of my many inventions. It was a wonderful automaton that amazed crowds in many of the great cities of Europe.'

Joe and Belle nodded.

'But did you know about the fire in the museum?' Joe asked.

'Yes, indeed I had heard about it, but you see it is not the mechanical chessmaster itself that I am seeking. I left that many, many years ago in a cellar in Berlin. It is the spirit of Kadir I have been searching for in vain, and now for no reason that I can understand the young Turk has come to you in this little shop.'

35

Joe leaned forward. 'He comes into my dreams as well. We play chess but I can never talk to him. Why is he dressed like the Turkish chessmaster? The chessmaster was just an automaton wasn't it?'

'Ah yes, but many automata become homes for spirits. I think you know that already.' He lifted his hand in a gesture towards the shelves. 'Like your old devil Mephisto and his companions. The automata provide a material body for the spirits to inhabit when they are in this world. They come and go and they use them when they need to.'

'A bit like a railway junction?' said Joe.

'Yes,' the old man smiled. 'You must understand that I am a scientist and an engineer but I also dabbled in the Black Arts, and spirits came to me; all sorts of spirits, young and old, dancers, and philosophers, those who had unfinished business in this world. One of these was a young man named Kadir from somewhere in the Ottoman lands, a lost spirit who came to me several times. In his lifetime he had been at the court, where he became a favourite of the Sultan before he was killed by a jealous rival. I played chess with him and I realised that he was a genius.'

'Yes, he's brilliant,' Joe nodded again. 'But why do you want to find him now?'

'Let me just say this. I made a promise to him once that I have not been able to keep, and I wish to put that right. Besides,' he paused and gave a croaky laugh, 'I believe that he has something very precious of mine. This is all part of a long story, and you,' he waved his claw-like hand at Joe and Belle, 'are now part of it. I would like to tell you more.

If you and your sister are able to leave your shop for a short while and come with me, I have something very important to show you.'

A warning flashed in Belle's mind. Mr Kempel still made her feel uncomfortable. We know almost nothing about him. She was about to make an excuse about not being able to leave the shop but Joe moved forward and answered immediately.

'Yes, I'll come. We can shut up the shop for a bit can't we, Belle?'

Belle was taken by surprise. 'I'm not sure it's a good idea,' she said. 'We're not even dressed yet.'

'That won't take long. Come on Belle, Uncle Griff will be really interested if we find out more about the mechanical chessmaster for him.'

Belle was dithering. It would be sensible to say that they couldn't leave the shop, but it'd be a shame to miss out on something as exciting as this. She was keen to find out more...

'OK,' she said, 'as long as we're not away from the shop too long.'

'Believe me, your uncle won't even notice that you are gone,' the old man assured her.

They dashed upstairs, pulled on their clothes and Belle wrote a note to Uncle Griff

Doing some research about the mechanical chessmaster.
Back by 10.30.

7

THE JOURNEY

THEY FOLLOWED MR KEMPEL'S TALL FIGURE out of the shop, past the bombed-out buildings and the weed-covered heaps of rubble into the fresh green of Tavistock Park.

Mr Kempel, with his long legs, strode out in front, remarkably quickly for an old man and Belle had to hurry to keep up. She glanced up at the tall London plane trees, now covered in tiny green leaf buds, their branches reaching high into the sky. But as they moved further into the park she had a strange feeling. The trees didn't look the same. The branches were thinner and the trunks closer together. With a prickle of fear she realised that the trees she was looking at no longer had any leaves on them at all. What's happening?

It was growing darker and colder. She wasn't in a London park any more but in a forest of delicate silver birch trees. The snow was thick on the ground and it was night time, stars sparkling through the branches, bitterly cold, and the wind blowing flakes of snow into her face.

'Joe, where are you?' She screamed as she gulped in the freezing air. She was on her own in the depths of an unknown forest and fear crept through her like the wind's icy fingers. What's happened to my brother?

'I'm here.' With a crash of branches and a shower of snow, Joe came rushing out through a wall of trees, nearly knocking her over.

She grabbed his hand. 'Oh Joe, I thought I'd lost you. Where've we come to? What is this place?'

He was shivering. 'It's like those pictures about wolves and I heard something howling out there.'

'It's deepest winter in a forest, and we're in a foreign country. Is this one of your other worlds?' She stared at Joe and realised that something else was different. He was wearing a stout pair of high boots, a heavy tunic and a fur hat which was too big for him. She was wrapped in a long, red cape with a fur-lined hood.

From behind her she heard the sound of hooves and turned round just in time to see a horse-drawn carriage speeding off along the forest track.

'Not just a different country, we're in a different time! Mr Kempel brought us here, but where's he gone?'

Joe shook his head. 'I don't know what to do now. It's freezing and I'm scared of those wolves.'

As he spoke Belle also heard a faint howl coming from the forest. 'We've got to move quickly. There's a light up there on the hill and I think that's where this path is leading to. We'd better follow it.'

The path through the trees did indeed take them to a wooden house with a low roof, surrounded by a wide veranda with icicles hanging from the eaves. As they walked up to the door Joe held up his hand to knock, but then put it down and turned round to Belle. 'But we don't know who lives here.'

'Oh come on,' said Belle, stamping her feet to keep warm. 'We can't stay out here or we'll freeze to death.' She gave three loud thumps on the door and it was opened immediately. There was a gust of warm air which smelt of food and a woman's voice called out. 'Come in; come in my little ones. We have been worried about you. Thank the good Lord that you have arrived safely. I am Maria, the housekeeper. Here, come in by the stove. I have made soup.' A large woman with a red face pulled them into the house and helped them with their coats. 'Come now, sit down, sit down, the Baron has just returned and he is anxious to see you.'

I don't know who she is or what she's talking about, thought Belle, suddenly feeling terribly tired, but the soup smells delicious and Joe looks as hungry as a wolf. She spooned the dark red soup into her mouth and let it trickle slowly into her stomach. Gradually the warmth spread through her body and pins and needles prickled in her finger tips as they turned back from fishy-white to pink. Where are we? How does this woman know us, or has she confused us with some other children? She stopped Maria as she swept past them, carrying pots and pans to one of the enormous cupboards.

'Thank you for the soup. It is delicious,' she said and paused. 'Can you just tell us where we are and whose house this is?'

Maria looked surprised. 'But of course, it is the house of Dr Orloff.' That didn't really help Belle and she looked blankly across at Joe. 'Who is Dr Orloff?'

'Oh, my poor little ones, you are confused,' said Maria. 'You have had a long journey and you must be very tired. Come now, if you are finished I will take you to the good doctor.' She guided them along a passage into the main room of the house.

As they opened the door Belle saw a familiar tall figure by the fire. It was Mr Kempel, but a younger, plumper Mr Kempel than the one they knew. Not a frail old man any more, his cheeks were pinker and his hair, though still rather thin, was a light brown colour.

'So he did come with us after all,' she whispered to Joe. 'He doesn't seem too worried about leaving us in the forest to freeze to death.'

'Or to the wolves!' Joe whispered back.

Certainly no concern showed in his face as he stepped forward to greet the children. 'Ah Jozef, Bella, how good that you have arrived safely. This is my dear friend Dr Orloff who has been teaching me the Russian language here in his comfortable home.'

Then turning to the doctor, 'These are the children I told you about. They are in my care for a while. I hope that they may stay here.'

The doctor was a big man with a thick brown beard. He held out his hands to the children with a welcoming smile.

'Jozef, Bella, I hope your journey to Russia has not been too tiring. You are welcome to stay and rest here. I understand that my friend, Baron von Kempelen, will be taking you with him to Vienna.'

'Indeed I will,' said the man they knew as Mr Kempel, 'I have an appointment with her majesty the Empress Maria Theresa of Austria.'

We're really going with him to the court in Vienna! Belle's face lit up with excitement.

She felt that she ought to say something polite to the doctor so she stepped forward and tried a rather clumsy curtsey which seemed the right thing to do.

'My brother and I are grateful for your invitation to stay in your house, sir. It is very kind of you.'

'Come,' he said. You must be very tired, Maria will take you to your bedroom.'

'But if you will excuse me, doctor,' interrupted Baron von Kempelen/Mr Kempel. 'Before the children go to bed I would like to introduce them to my creation, who will be their travelling companion. Come this way.' He guided Joe and Belle into a small back room.

There, sitting behind a large wooden cabinet was a model of a man with a black pointed beard and long droopy moustache, just as they had seen in the magazine picture. His red and gold robes looked heavy and rich and were trimmed with light brown fur. He was holding his hand out towards a set of red and white ivory chessmen.

'He looks much grander than in the picture, doesn't he?' whispered Joe. 'But the eyes are glass and they're empty.'

'So, my young friends,' said Baron von Kempelen. 'What do you think of my invention?'

'It's wonderful,' said Joe. 'But the spirit of the young Turk – Kadir, the one who comes to the shop – he's not here is he?'

The Baron shook his head. 'No, no. This is only the beginning of the story. For now he is a free spirit. He comes and goes as he pleases.' He smiled. 'Be patient, young man. If you wish you may watch the automaton play chess against Dr Orloff tomorrow.'

8

CAPTAIN
ALEKSY WOROUSKY

THE FEATHER BEDS WERE WONDERFULLY comfortable, and both children slept soundly that night. When Belle woke, her first thought was that she was in her bed in the shop, but she took a quick glance around the room and memory came flooding back. A china jug and basin stood on a stand beside the bed and there were two brass candle sticks on the table. It's all still here. We're really in Russia. She hugged herself with excitement as she remembered their journey.

Joe was still fast asleep, so she slipped out of bed, her toes poking out under her long nightgown, drew back the heavy curtains and looked out at the outline of birch trees against a pale pink sky. A path through the trees led down to a frozen lake which, like the snow, was tinged with streaks of pink and gold. As she watched, a small flock of wild geese took off from the lake and flew across the sky. 'How beautiful,' she murmured.

Underneath the window she could see a wooden veranda which had been cleared of snow and she heard the tap-tap of a stick. Someone was walking early in the morning. The man who came round the corner of the house was dressed in a dark blue military coat trimmed with red and gold. He walked with stiff legs, leaning heavily on the sticks that he held in both hands. The walking seemed to cost him some effort and, as he paused under her window for a rest, Belle made a slight noise with the clasp of the window frame which made him look up. Instead of the old man she had expected, she saw a young and handsome face, very pale with thick brown hair. His eyes were a grey-blue and he looked straight up at her, as if asking a question. Then, as though that was somehow not the right thing to do, he looked away, gave a polite and apologetic bow and moved on, tapping with his sticks along the veranda.

Belle felt her heart beating fast. Who is he?

There was a movement from the feather bed as Joe woke up and stretched. 'What's going on? Where are we?'

Belle pulled herself away from the window and took a deep breath.

'Well it seems that we are with Baron von Kempelen, otherwise known as Mr Kempel, in Russia and we're going to be travelling with him and the Turkish chessmaster to the Empress's Court in Vienna. How does that sound?'

'Crazy,' said Joe. 'When I woke up I thought I'd been dreaming.'

'It's not a dream,' said Belle. 'It all seems very real. But I can't help feeling worried. I'd really love to go to Vienna.

It would be such a great adventure, but what about Uncle Griff? He won't know where we are and he'll be anxious about us. We can't just disappear without telling him.'

'I've been thinking about that too,' said Joe, 'but it's OK. We're in a different time zone from Uncle Griff now. I've travelled back once before, you see.'

Belle felt a shiver of alarm. 'What do you mean? When? Why didn't you tell me?'

'It was when I was at the Benions. I so wanted to get away from them that I was wishing I was somewhere else and I just found myself back in a different time and I stayed there for a while. I would've come back of course. But that's the thing you see. You never even knew that I'd gone, did you? So when we get back to London, it'll seem as though we'd never left and Uncle Griff won't have been worried at all. I suppose it's a bit like being in a dream, but we're both in it together.'

He held out his hand to Belle. 'I'm so glad that you're here. I really want to go to Vienna too. Let's see what happens.' He jumped out of bed and ran to the window. 'Wow! Just look at all that snow!'

A wooden chest full of clothes stood by the bed and Belle pulled out a dark red woollen dress. It had a long, full skirt and was trimmed with fur at the wrists. She knew immediately that it would fit her and she pulled it over her head. It was soft and warm. She pulled on her boots, brushed her dark hair and tied it back from her face with a ribbon.

Joe was looking at her from the window seat. 'You look lovely, Belle,' he said.

Belle laughed, 'Well it's better than that horrible old skirt and jumper I always used to wear. Come on, Joe, get dressed and we can go downstairs and find out what's going on.'

After breakfast they all went into the side room with Dr Orloff. Joe couldn't wait to see the automaton actually play a game of chess.

Baron von Kempelen, as they now knew him, was standing by the door and showed them to their seats. Belle and Joe were tucked into a corner seat where they had a very clear view of the chessboard.

'Just look at the Baron,' she whispered. 'He's really pleased with his invention. He can't wait to show it off.'

'Ahem,' the Baron coughed for silence. 'Allow me to introduce my invention. As you, Dr Orloff, know, I am very interested in automata and have long believed that such cunningly constructed machines will eventually perform in a way that is superior to humans. The triumph of this, the first machine to think, as you will now witness, is that it is capable of winning a game against the most accomplished chess players. Now, Dr Orloff, if you will oblige? Let me demonstrate before you take your seat, that nothing is concealed in the cabinet.'

Belle was quite close to the cabinet and she looked very closely as the Baron opened the three doors one by one. The first just showed a collection of wheels and cogs.

'It looks like the inside of a clock,' said Joe.

When the second door was opened Belle could see right through the cabinet to the paper on the wall behind

47

it. The third compartment was clearly empty apart from a red cushion.

She shook her head at Joe. 'There's definitely no one in there.'

'Sh! I want to listen,' said her brother.

The Baron was moving round to the side of the automaton. He put a large key into a hole in the side of the cabinet, and wound up the mechanism with a loud ratcheting sound.

Once he had stopped turning the key there was silence.

'Oh no, it's not working,' whispered Joe.

But after a pause Belle could hear the sound of whirring and grinding clockwork, like a clock about to chime, coming from inside the automaton. The carved wooden figure slowly turned its head from side to side as though looking at the chessboard. Then suddenly it lurched into life, reaching out with his left arm and moving one of the chessmen forward.

'Ho, ho, magnificent my dear friend,' called Dr Orloff. 'Now for my move.'

'Dr Orloff's a good player,' whispered Joe, after watching a few moves, 'but I think the automaton may win this game.'

Every now and then the Baron went back to the left-hand side of the cabinet to wind up the clockwork mechanism.

'Dr Orloff's losing,' Joe whispered again. 'I think I know what the automaton's next move will be. It could be checkmate.'

Sure enough, after his next move, the automaton nodded his head three times to signal checkmate.

'Damn me,' said Dr Orloff. 'I'm beaten. Your Turk is a very fine player. Well done indeed. It is an excellent invention and I am sure that it will impress the Viennese court.'

'Now,' said the Baron, 'if you will all move to the next room, I will attend to the machine and will join you there shortly.'

'So what did you think, young Jozef?' Dr Orloff asked as they left the room.

'The Turk plays aggressively,' said Joe, 'I think you would need a very strong opening.'

'Ah,' said the doctor, 'so you are a chess player too. You must meet Captain Aleksy Worousky. He is always looking for a game. I wonder where he is, I haven't seen him this morning. I thought he would have wanted to watch the automaton play.'

Belle sat on a window seat and looked out at the snow covered countryside stretching away for miles. She was surprised at how calm she felt. Being here in a foreign country in a different time didn't seem so very strange. She felt safe in this house and the thought of going to Vienna was really exciting. She didn't notice when the Baron came back into the room but she did hear the tap-tap of sticks and turned round quickly to see the soldier from earlier that morning standing in the doorway.

'Allow me to introduce you to our new guests, Jozef and Bella,' said Dr Orloff. 'This brave soldier is Captain

Aleksy Worousky. He is staying here with us until he is well enough to return to Poland.'

The Captain smiled and bowed to both children. 'Ah,' he said, 'the little lady at the window this morning.'

Belle felt a blush burning her cheeks. She lowered her eyes and muttered, 'I am very pleased to meet you.' Then turned quickly back to the window.

But Dr Orloff seemed in a hurry to talk to the Captain and she listened carefully from her window seat.

'Well, Captain, I have just been soundly beaten at chess by an automaton, what say you to that?'

'I have heard that it is indeed a marvellous invention,' he replied.

'However,' continued the doctor, 'two things are puzzling me. The first is that the automaton played a game remarkably like your own. The second is that you, who have been so interested in it up to now, were not there to watch its first game, but appear suddenly when it is over. I can't help wondering whether in some way it was you who were playing me this morning, but I cannot work out how you did it.'

Belle turned round in time to see a broad smile on Captain Aleksy's face as he looked over to the Baron.

'Ah Baron, I think we have been discovered,' he said. 'Yes, it was indeed I who beat you this morning, Dr Orloff.'

'But how did you do it? It was clear that the cabinet was totally empty. We were shown all the compartments.'

I knew it, thought Belle. There had to be a chess player hiding in the cabinet somehow.

50

'Do not forget that the Baron, as well as being a man of science, is also a conjurer,' smiled the Captain. 'The cabinet is very carefully constructed to appear to be empty, but that is a trick and I can move inside it without being seen. So, when one door is opened, I have already moved to the next partition. When the Baron winds up the mechanism it is only to drown the sound of my movements.'

Belle was listening to the conversation and she couldn't help smiling. So that was it, a conjuring trick! But she found his next words disturbing.

Moving closer to the doctor and speaking rather more quietly the Captain said, 'Of course by removing the excellent legs that you made for me, I have much more room to move. But that is only part of the plan. The Baron has made a special cart which will take the cabinet, in which I can also travel, unseen to the frontier. That way I may be able to avoid the Russian soldiers who are searching for me and who are anxious to claim the reward that has been placed upon my head.'

Dr Orloff looked serious. 'May God be with you and protect you, my dear young man.' he said. 'I will miss you. It has given me pleasure to see you regain your health after such serious injury and I greatly admire your courage.'

Belle thought she heard tears in his voice as he patted the young soldier's back.

Joe had crept up beside Belle on the window seat and as the adults turned away he whispered to her. 'So is the chess master a fake after all? Was that soldier hiding in the cabinet?'

Belle nodded. Then she heard the Baron's voice.

'We plan to leave tomorrow. It is a long journey to Vienna and we will have to travel slowly to save our poor friend Aleksy from too much discomfort in his cart. If asked, we will explain that we are travelling so slowly to protect the delicate mechanism of the machine. We will stop to give several performances in the towns we pass through on the route to avoid suspicion.'

He turned to Belle and Joe. 'You, my young friends, will share the triumph of our presentation at the Viennese court.'

9

THE RUSSIAN ARMY

THE SOUND OF HAMMERING WOKE BELLE THE
following morning. The sun had barely risen and in the pale
light of dawn she could see soft flakes of snow blowing
against her window.

'Wake up, Joe, something's happening.'

In the courtyard below several workers, well wrapped
up against the cold, were building what looked like wooden
shelves into a large four-wheeled cart. Captain Aleksy was
standing by, giving instructions and next to him, his red
velvet robes blowing in the icy wind, was the wooden
model of the Turkish chessmaster. As they watched, the
cabinet was carefully lifted onto the cart.

'They're getting ready to go,' said Joe. 'Captain Aleksy's
going to be hidden in the cart with the cabinet and the
chessmaster.'

Belle looked down at the thin figure of the Captain, who
was swinging his arms across his chest to keep warm. She
hated to think of his long journey cooped up in that little cart.

'He's going to be really uncomfortable and cold in there,' she said. 'He did say that he wouldn't have to be there for the whole journey, but I don't know how long it'll be until he feels safe to come into the coach with us.'

'Why's he hiding from the Russian soldiers anyway?' Joe asked. 'Dr Orloff is Russian and we're in Russia now aren't we? So how come the Russians are enemies?'

Belle shrugged her shoulders. 'Captain Aleksy's Polish, perhaps they're fighting against the Russians, but I don't know. We might get a chance to ask him on the journey. Come on let's go downstairs I can smell food and I'm hungry.'

Following a lovely smell of freshly baked bread they came to the kitchen door but were nearly knocked down by Maria, followed by a line of servants, carrying large hampers of food out to the courtyard. 'Not in here, little ones,' she said. 'We're all in too much of a spin packing up for the journey. Breakfast is waiting for you in the library.'

From the library window they watched the bags being loaded onto the coach, and saw Maria and Dr Orloff come out with armfuls of cushions and fur-lined wraps. Belle was pleased to see that some of these were put into the cart for Aleksy.

The Baron was striding up and down in his long grey coat, giving instructions to the servants, and supervising the packing. He kept checking and rechecking the cart which held the chessmaster's cabinet. He looks anxious, thought Belle. His precious chessmaster is at risk.

Finally she heard the sound of hooves on the cobbles as the stable lads brought the horses round to be harnessed to the coach.

The door was flung open and Maria rushed in carrying warm coats and hats for them. 'Come on, come on, it's time to go,' she said. 'Here you are, my dear, this will keep your little hands warm,' she passed Belle a beautiful fur muff. 'Now, I filled up the bottle inside with hot water and you can fill it again whenever you make a stop at an inn.'

'You've been so kind to us Maria,' said Belle giving her a hug. 'I wish you were coming too.'

'Oh no, I've too much to do here, my dears, looking after the doctor and all his waifs and strays,' she said, smiling. But then she dropped her voice.

'You know that Captain Aleksy is in grave danger on this journey, don't you? That is why the good Baron is hiding him in the cart.'

'But why's it so dangerous?' asked Joe.

Maria pulled the children closer to her and whispered. 'There is a price on his head. Our Captain is a brave young man who led his Polish regiment in a revolt against the Russian soldiers. So the Russian army will be looking for him. You children must help to protect him along the way. Do not talk to anyone about your passenger, you understand?'

Belle wasn't sure that she did understand, but she nodded anyway. There was no time to ask any more questions as the Baron swept into the library. 'Good morning, Bella, Jozef, I trust you slept well. We must leave now. We hope to reach the border by tomorrow.'

The two children were helped up the step into the coach and snuggled down into the soft cushions. Maria pointed out the hamper of provisions on the floor between them. Baron von Kempelen swung himself up onto the seat beside the driver. There were goodbyes and a crack of the whip and then they were off.

The road was very straight, cutting through thick forest on either side. Occasionally they saw a wooden house in a clearing and once they passed through a village with a church and a few villagers, who stared as they went past.

All along the road there were soldiers, marching in columns. Belle felt a flicker of alarm each time she saw them, but everything seemed peaceful until late that afternoon when they heard the boom of cannon fire and the shrill whinnying of horses in the distance.

'Can you hear that Belle? There's a battle going on and it's not far away.'

Joe looked out of the window, then quickly pulled his head back inside. 'Hey, they're coming this way. Russian soldiers, I think, about five of them. The coach is stopping.'

Belle froze. She sat on the edge of her seat, her fists clenched, nails digging into the palms of her hands. There were loud voices, commands, the sound of horses being pulled up. A red face with a large moustache appeared at the window, stared at her for a moment, then moved round to the front of the coach where Baron von Kempelen was sitting with the driver. The voice was rough and threatening.

'Captain Glazkov of the Imperial Russian Army, 10th division. I am required to ask you what your business is and where you are travelling to. What are you carrying in that cart?'

It was a relief to hear the Baron's cool reply.

'The cart is carrying a marvellous invention which was commissioned by the Empress Maria Theresa and is being taken to Vienna to be presented at her court. It is a chess-playing automaton. We are travelling slowly so that it will not be damaged. Here are my papers. I am Baron von Kempelen from Hungary; these children are my nephew and niece who will be helping me to present my invention at court.'

'The soldier's going round the back,' whispered Joe. 'He's going to look in the cart.'

Belle pushed up beside him at the window. Five soldiers on horseback were drawn up behind the cart; their swords raised. The lid was open and the commanding officer was poking around inside.

'Aleksy's hidden underneath the chessmaster isn't he?' whispered Joe.

Belle nodded 'He's in a special compartment, so they might not see him, but those soldiers are much too close!'

She clung tightly to the edge of the window. What will they do if they find him, drag him away? Kill him?

At that moment something extraordinary happened. From inside the open cart a turbaned figure rose slowly into the air. The apparition towered above the soldiers, with its arms open wide and its bright flowing robes shimmering in a strange, ghostly light.

There were cries of alarm as the soldiers moved back, some of them hastily making the sign of the cross. Their horses whinnied in fear as they reared up and two of them bolted, carrying their riders with them.

'It's Kadir!' Joe could, hardly keep his voice down. 'He is here after all. Fantastic!'

The Russian officer jumped back from the cart with a curse.

'This is necromancy, and I will have nothing to do with it,' he shouted at the Baron. 'Be on your way, but I warn you, if I catch you on these roads again you will find yourself and all your evil contraptions under lock and key.'

He signalled to his remaining soldiers and they rode off down the road. Belle heard the driver crack his whip and the coach trundled on again. She was almost crying with relief. It's all over! Aleksy's safe. I was so sure they'd find him and... she couldn't bear to think about what might have happened. It was some time before she could breathe easily again and panic shot through her every time she heard the sound of horses' hooves, but thankfully they saw no more of the Russian army.

10

THE ROAD TO VIENNA

THE ROAD TO VIENNA WENT ON AND ON AND
on.

Once they had crossed the Russian border, Captain
Aleksy felt safe to travel in the coach with Belle and Joe.

'This is a long journey,' he said with a smile. 'I trust
we will not be interrupted any more by those ill-mannered
Russian soldiers. As we are now fellow conspirators,
perhaps we can share some secrets? May I ask where you are
from and why you are travelling with Baron von Kempelen?'

Belle looked at Joe, and he gave a nod as if to say 'tell
him'.

'We are from London,' she hesitated and decided not say
'in 1944', but she added, 'our parents were killed in the war.'

She saw the sadness in his eyes and her throat tightened,
making it difficult to go on. She swallowed hard but her
voice sounded croaky. 'I try not to think about them.'

The Captain's voice was very gentle. 'I am so sorry.
There are too many wars in Europe and so many children

have lost their families. You are very brave to come so far from home, but who cares for you?'

He feels sorry for us. Belle couldn't remember anyone feeling sorry for them before. She wanted to tell him the whole truth, but she didn't know how to explain.

'Belle does,' said Joe, and then, seeing the surprise on the Captain's face, 'Well we have an uncle, but we don't really know yet if he can look after us or not.'

'And Baron von Kempelen, is he perhaps a guardian?'

'No,' said Joe. 'We don't actually know why the Baron wants us to travel with him. But he likes us to be his assistants when he presents the chessmaster. Can I ask you a question now?' Aleksy nodded.

'Why did you fight the Russians?'

'That is easy to answer. Because they marched into my country. What else could I do?'

'But why did Dr Orloff help you? He's Russian isn't he?'

This time Aleksy took longer to answer. 'Dr Orloff is a true doctor, who helps the sick and wounded, from any country. He was looking for survivors after the battle and he found me lying in a ditch. I was the only one. All my companions were dead. As you know, he saved my life. It was his idea to ask Baron von Kempelen to smuggle me out of Russia. There is a price on my head because I led my regiment to mutiny and the Russians are looking for me, so you see the Turk's cabinet was an excellent way out.'

He's so brave. How terrible to lay all night in that ditch, badly wounded. Belle had tears in her eyes.

He smiled. 'Don't look so sad, little Bella. I am alive. I will play chess for the Baron for a time. Somehow I will get back to Poland and one day my country will be free. You see my poor Poland is in the middle of Europe. It is such a beautiful country. Our people love music and stories and dancing and poetry. We want only to be left alone, but there are greedy giants on our borders who want our land. Do you know how big Russia is?' He held out his arms as wide as he could. 'So big! Why do they want our land?'

He laughed. 'But enough sad talk. We will soon be in Vienna, which is a beautiful city and we will have good fun fooling the Austrian Court. Jozef, I hear you are a chess player. Shall we have a game?'

As the days passed Belle grew tired of being cooped up in the coach. The constant bumping of the wheels was making her back ache and the way the coach swayed on its springs made her feel sick. She slept a lot and woke each time to the same view of snow- covered trees and pale sun.

One afternoon, while Belle was dreamily thinking about Vienna, she dropped off to sleep and woke to find that she had slipped sideways onto Aleksy's shoulder. It took a few seconds for her to realise where she was. Her nose was pressed against his army jacket which smelled of the outside, of mud and wood smoke. She felt so comfortable lying there that she kept her eyes closed. From the corner of her eye she had glimpsed Joe curled up, also fast asleep, on the opposite seat.

Aleksy and the Baron were talking in soft voices.

'Young Jozef is an excellent chess player,' she heard Aleksy say. 'Are you planning to use him to play chess in the automaton?'

'No, not yet,' replied the Baron, 'although it would be useful to have him on hand if for some reason you cannot play. Perhaps you could teach him how to operate the chessmaster?'

Belle felt pleased for Joe, she knew he would like that, but the rest of the Baron's reply puzzled her. 'That is not why I brought him here,' the Baron continued, 'the boy has some connection with the spirit of the young Turkish chess player, Kadir. It is not clear to me at this moment and I do not fully understand what the connection is. Perhaps he has some special knowledge. We will see.'

'But they are just children.' Aleksy's voice was warm and worried.

'Don't worry, my kind-hearted friend. Trust me. They will come to no harm.' The Baron laughed softly. 'The girl guards her brother as if he were her own cub. I can tell that she has strength, and the boy has his own special gifts. For some reason the spirit, Kadir, visits him.'

He leaned forward and spoke even more quietly. 'I do not believe the Turkish spirit would have come to your rescue on the road if he were not concerned for the boy's safety. He comes and goes as he pleases and I am not able to summon him at my own will.'

Belle could feel Aleksy breathe out slowly, 'I owe him my life then. But my dear Baron, I have something I must say to you. In times of war we fail to protect our children.

They are so precious and they are our future. These children have suffered already. If they are in your care I trust you do not take that lightly.'

Belle thought the Baron was about to reply but the conversation stopped abruptly as Joe woke up. He stretched himself and looked out of the window. 'Hey, come and look Belle, the river's really wide now and there are lots of boats on it.'

'We're following the Danube River,' Aleksy said. 'Those boats are carrying goods into Vienna. It won't be long now until we arrive there ourselves.'

As the afternoon drew to a close and the setting sun turned the snowy fields pink, Belle saw the spires and domes of churches in the distance. There were lots of carts and carriages on the road now and more and more boats moving along the broad river carrying sacks of provisions for the town. The road became busier and noisier as the coach took them through the city gates and into wide streets of tall buildings. For the first time Belle felt the jolt of cobblestones under the wheels. Then at last she heard the coachman shout to the horses and they stopped outside a handsome stone house.

'This is where we will be staying,' said the Baron, as he helped Belle down from the coach. 'It is not far from the Palace of Schönbrunn where we will be presenting the chessmaster to the Empress tomorrow. I hope you have not found the journey too tiring.'

Several servants had already arrived at the door and were unloading bags from the coach. Belle felt so stiff and tired, she could hardly walk up the winding staircase to their room. There, she and Joe found nightgowns laid out for them on beautifully draped beds and a small meal and a drink of milk set out for them on a table. She sank into the comfort of the fresh sheets. What's going to happen tomorrow? She asked herself. She was looking forward to seeing the palace and hoped the Empress would be pleased with the chessmaster. Is anyone going to guess that it's a fake? Before she had time to answer any of these questions she drifted into a deep sleep.

11

THE SCHÖNBRUNN PALACE

'ALEKSY SAYS THE EMPRESS MARIA THERESA herself will be there today,' said Joe as they drank cups of hot chocolate in their bedroom next morning. 'She'll be choosing someone from her court to play against our chessmaster. The Baron wants to show everyone how amazing he is.'

'How does Aleksy make his moves?' asked Belle, who hadn't been able to look closely at the automaton.

'Oh he showed me last time we stopped. There are levers inside the cabinet which control the model's left arm. The levers move the arm up and down and if Aleksy turns the lever it opens and closes the model's hand so that he can grasp the pieces on the board and make his next move. Aleksy told me he had to practice quite a lot before he got the hang of it, but he finds it easy now.'

'It must be uncomfortable for him in there,' said Belle.

'He says it is not too bad. Without his wooden legs he doesn't need much space, but it gets very hot, and sometimes he gets cramp. If he really needs to move, he taps gently on the back of the cabinet and the Baron winds up the machinery to hide any noise he makes. We'll be helping the Baron move the cabinet on and off the stage and get Aleksy out.'

'Are you excited, Joe?' asked Belle.

'Yes, but I'm a bit worried too. What if it all goes wrong and the Empress finds out that it's a hoax? Do you think she might throw us in a dungeon or something?'

'I hadn't thought about that,' admitted Belle. 'I suppose we just have to trust the Baron. He seems to know what he is doing.'

As it turned out, the Empress Maria Theresa would be delighted with the Baron's invention. It was Belle who was disappointed with the Empress. She had imagined a beautiful elegant lady and saw instead a dumpy person with grey hair and several double chins, who reminded her of one of the teachers at school, except that the Empress was dressed in layers of beautiful lace, covered in jewels, and surrounded by bowing courtiers.

'She does look quite clever though, doesn't she?' She whispered to Joe. 'I wonder if she'll guess.'

A few specially invited guests were gathered in the beautifully painted ballroom of the Schönbrunn Palace, waiting to watch the first match with the 'amazing mechanical chessmaster', and Belle felt her heart racing as she and Joe helped the Baron to bring the cabinet in from the side room and wheel it onto the stage.

With a gesture of her hand the Empress indicated that he should begin and the Baron stepped forward, with his usual speech.

'My Empress and honoured guests. This is a machine that can think, the like of which has never been seen before, an automaton which not only plays chess, but is superior to the most expert players in the world.'

Belle heard a murmur of disbelief run through the audience.

The Baron heard it too. 'In case any of you have any doubts about the authenticity of this amazing invention, I will now display the inner workings of the machine.'

'This bit is really clever, isn't it?' said Joe. 'You can't believe that there is actually anyone inside.'

Sure enough the audience seemed convinced, and after the Baron had closed all the doors of the cabinet and placed the chessmen on the board he announced:

'The automaton is ready to play chess. Is anyone in the audience prepared to challenge it to game?'

An elegantly dressed young man stood up.

'Ah Count Cobenzyl,' said the Baron, 'I would be honoured if you would play chess with my automaton; I know that Your Excellency is a skilled chess player.' The count acknowledged this with a slight bow and – nervously, Belle thought – made his way to the cabinet to seat himself in front of the chessmaster.

As the Baron turned the key in the side of the cabinet, the whirring clockwork sound started up and the audience murmured to each other as the automaton slowly turned his head from side to side and reached over to move his piece. The game had begun.

'I'm not sure the count is such a skilled chess player after all,' whispered Joe after a few moves. 'I don't think it will be a tough match for Aleksy.' Sure enough, not long afterwards Belle saw the chessmaster nod his head three times. 'Check mate,' muttered Joe, 'I knew it.'

The count, looking embarrassed and annoyed, made his way back to the audience where he muttered in a low voice to his companions. The Empress, however, was clearly impressed.

'I congratulate you, Baron von Kempelen. You promised me that you would construct a machine that would be far more surprising than the performances of all the conjurors and dabblers in magnetism which we have recently seen at court, and I consider that you have done so.'

With that she left the room, followed by most of her courtiers. Belle looked at the Baron to see if he was pleased by the Empress's remarks, but she couldn't tell anything from his expression.

However, at dinner that night the Baron congratulated Captain Aleksy.

'Well he didn't play much of a game,' admitted Aleksy. 'I think the audience made him nervous. I must confess I was nervous too, but I am glad that it is over. Shall we move on tomorrow?'

'We shall see,' said the Baron. 'You must not be in too much of a hurry, young man.'

But they did not move on tomorrow, or the next day, or the one after that. The chessmaster's fame spread throughout Vienna and the Empress insisted that Baron von Kempelen should continue to present his shows, so that news of his wonderful invention would reach the rest of Europe.

Belle and Joe helped the Baron to present the chessmaster every evening at the Schönbrunn Palace, but during the day they were free to wander in the beautiful palace gardens or to walk down to the river. They often met Captain Aleksy in the gardens. He spent several hours each day practising with his sticks and was getting much better at walking.

'At this rate I will be challenging you to a race soon,' he said to Joe one morning. It was a beautiful sunny day, and winter seemed to be moving on.

Joe laughed. 'You can't beat me at chess *and* at running, that wouldn't be fair.'

The three went on together towards the river and Belle felt a glow of happiness, just walking beside him.

'I wonder what Baron von Kempelen does all day,' she said. 'He never seems to be around.'

'Oh he has much scheming to do at the palace,' Aleksy said with a laugh. 'He is an important man and something of a favourite with the Empress, but he has many rivals.'

'Do you trust the Baron?' Belle blurted out suddenly, thinking of the conversation she'd overheard in the coach.

Aleksy looked surprised. 'That is a very good question for you to ask, and I will try to answer it honestly. I had to trust the Baron. There was no other way. I would not have got out of Russia alive without him.'

He paused. 'I do not think he is a bad man, but I think that he is a man who always works for himself. Do you understand what I mean? He is not like Dr Orloff, who helps people without any thought for himself. No,' he smiled, 'I do not think our Baron is like that. True, he helped me to escape because I am very useful to him. But he will not betray me and I trust him to keep his promise to help me return to Poland soon.

'What about you, Jozef and Bella? You must have trust in the Baron as you came to Russia with him. What do you know about him?'

'Well that's just it,' said Belle. 'We don't really know much. We think it was the spirit of the chessmaster, Kadir, who found Joe. The Baron followed him to our shop.'

'That is interesting. Shall we rest for a while?' He pointed to a stone bench. 'I will tell you something that I have told no one else. I have never actually seen the spirit. When he scared the Russian troops with such a magnificent act, I was hiding at the bottom of the cart, but I have felt his presence. When I played that first game at the palace with Count Cobenzyl I played a wrong move. As soon as I made the move I knew it was wrong, but to my surprise when I looked at the board, I saw that the chess piece had been moved from the square where I had placed it to another square. It must have been the spirit who corrected my error, but I don't think the Baron even knew that I had been helped.'

'If the spirit can operate the automaton and he's such a brilliant player, why doesn't the Baron use him all the time?' asked Joe.

Aleksy shrugged his shoulders. 'Baron von Kempelen is a man of many skills. He is very ambitious and would stop at little to make his inventions successful. I believe he has acquired some of the Black Arts of Magic and has used them to trap this spirit but, as you see, he cannot always control him, so he doesn't know whether he will appear or not.'

He bent his head towards the children and spoke softly. 'I think it is for Jozef's friendship with the spirit that the Baron has brought you here, and I would advise you to be careful. The Black Arts can be very dangerous for those who practice them. I have heard that spirits sometimes try to take the ones they love back to the spirit world with them.'

Then he made the sign of the cross, just as the Russian soldiers had done 'Protect us all from evil spirits,' he said.

Joe protested immediately. 'No, no, Kadir isn't like that, I know he isn't. He isn't an evil spirit and I'm not at all afraid of him.'

'I understand he is your friend, and he certainly saved my life, but please remember what I said.' Aleksy pushed himself slowly up from the bench onto his sticks. 'Now I think I will go back to the house, Jozef. I want to practise a new opening move, will you come with me?'

Left on her own, Belle looked across at the tall slim trees of the park at the edge of the gardens and the elegant townspeople strolling along the pathways. The women's long coats swept the ground and their hats were decorated with enormous feathers. Slightly mad, she thought, but how beautiful! The children were dressed like little grown-ups and had to walk quietly beside them. No rushing over the grass barefoot, as she and Joe would have done. She felt the soft warmth of the coming spring in the air although the trees were still bare of leaves. In the background she could hear the clip-clop of horses' hooves, drawing expensive carriages up to the Schönbrunn Palace.

But something made her stop to listen more carefully. What was that? Her ears were picking up a different sound in the distance. It sounded like traffic, like London traffic. The scene in the park seemed to be shifting and dimly, as though looking through a dirty window, she could make out a different scene; a park where the trees were in full leaf, children in short trousers played football, and she just caught a glimpse of a red London bus. Then, as quickly as it had come, it all disappeared.

It's London. It's still there! That must be the way back through the park!

Her first thought was that she must tell Joe straight away, but then she stopped herself.

No, we can't go back just yet. The Turkish chessmaster is at the palace again this evening, and all Vienna is talking about it. We just have to be there.

12

THE FINAL GAME AT THE SCHÖNBRUNN

THAT EVENING, AS BELLE WALKED DOWN TO the hallway, she watched her feet one by one on the stairs poking out under the hem of her lovely dress. They wore satin slippers embroidered with tiny pearls, dainty and elegant. The thought of her own scuffed brown school lace–ups made her smile, and she felt a thrill of excitement at the promise of the evening ahead.

Aleksy, in his smart dress uniform, was standing at the foot of the wide stairs, waiting for the carriage to take them to the palace. As Belle came to the last step, he held out his arm with mock formality and gave a little bow.

Looking at her dress, he smiled. 'Ah Bella, *bellisima*,' he said.

Belle felt her cheeks getting hot and was glad when he turned away from her towards the door.

'Come now, where is Jozef? We cannot be late,' he said. 'After all we must not forget that we are conspirators, not courtiers.'

Belle took her place with Joe, waiting to help the Baron move the cabinet from the side room onto the centre stage. Heavy red curtains decorated with gold stitching hung on each side of the stage to hide the entrance from the side room and a pair of large and highly decorated bronze urns had been placed one on each side. The crowd moved around, chatting noisily. Footmen in smart uniforms were passing round trays of sparkling glasses.

'Watch the crowd for me,' the Baron had said. 'I want to know if there are any trouble-makers tonight.'

'What about those ones over there?' Joe whispered to Belle, pointing out a group of elegantly dressed young men 'They seem a bit noisy.'

'They're certainly drinking a lot and they look as if they want people to notice them. They keep turning round to make sure everyone is looking.'

'The palace guards don't seem very interested,' Joe laughed, pointing to the two standing by the door at the far end of the ballroom. 'Look, they can't stop yawning.'

Just then Baron von Kempelen appeared from behind the curtain and the crowd quickly went quiet. Some took their seats at the little tables, others remained standing.

'Good evening, honoured guests. I welcome you to another demonstration of this remarkable machine. Do we have a challenger to play the chessmaster this evening?'

A young man stood up in the audience. Belle recognised him from the group of friends who had surrounded Count Cobenzyl on the first night. He was also of the group that she had noticed noisily drinking.

'I will play the chessmaster,' he said.

Belle glanced at the expressions on the faces of the young man's companions. 'I don't think it's a friendly challenge,' she whispered.

'I will play the chessmaster,' he said again. 'And I will also wager a considerable sum on behalf of my friends that the automaton will be beaten.' He strode up to the cabinet and threw a heavy purse onto the board.

The Baron calmly counted the coins.

'I accept your challenge and your wager,' he said, but he didn't sound very impressed. 'May I know your name?'

'My name is Count Johannes,' said the young man haughtily as he took his place at the table.

While the Baron went through the usual performance of opening the doors of the cabinet, Belle noticed the count watching them with particular care. Where is Aleksy hiding? She could never get rid of the twist of anxiety in her stomach, the fear that he might somehow be discovered and revealed to the whole crowd. But the young man sat down quickly to begin the game.

It was an even speedier defeat than usual. Count Johannes got up quickly from his chair, left the stage and joined his friends who were now standing in an aggressive group.

After a quick consultation with them he spoke.

'We are convinced, Baron von Kempelen, that your contraption is a fake. There is a hidden chess player in the machine. As I was defeated by unfair means, we therefore insist that you pay us your wager.'

Belle hardly dared to breathe. 'What do they know?' She couldn't look at Joe in case she gave something away.

But the Baron appeared totally calm as usual.

'My dear sir,' he said in a mocking tone, 'I do not understand. Where do you think I have hidden a chess player? Have I not already shown you all the empty compartments?'

Suddenly Belle saw something that made her heart stop. The count had taken out a small pistol and was aiming it straight at the cabinet.

'If they are empty, then no harm will be done if I have some target practice,' he said. 'Or would you prefer to pay the wager?'

Pay the wager, anything, pay the wager, it's Aleksy's life. Belle screamed inside.

Again the Baron's voice was unruffled. 'You have lost the game fairly, Count Johannes, and I do not owe you your wager. If you shoot into the cabinet you will damage the mechanism, which is extremely complicated and took many months to build. I must ask you not to do so.'

As the Baron looked towards the back of the hall, Belle saw that he had made a small gesture to the two palace guards who were positioned at the door, and they were moving forward through the crowd. The young man looked very angry now and his face was flushed. He's been drinking, thought Belle and he's showing off to his friends. He's going to fire his pistol, I'm sure he is. We must give the guards time? Smoke, a pretend fire, anything to distract them.

She pulled off her fine muslin shawl and thrust it into the bronze urn, then grabbing a candle set it alight. It caught quickly and smoke billowed out from behind the curtain.

'Come on Joe,' she called, and they ran onto the stage shouting 'Fire, fire!'

Immediately the crowd panicked and started rushing towards the doors. The count and his friends were caught up in the stampede and Belle saw the pistol knocked out of his hand. Then her heart leapt as she saw the palace guards arrive and escort him from the room.

Quickly Belle and Joe helped the Baron push the cabinet behind the curtains and Belle just had time to see the Baron help Aleksy out before she heard a loud military voice.

'Who has created this fire in the urn? I understand that some children started the fire. Where are they?'

Belle looked at the Baron. In his dark eyes she thought she saw a brief flash of admiration, and then he made a quick movement with his hand. Belle understood, it meant 'Go'.

She just had time to glance at Aleksy. He looked hot, dishevelled and shaken but he was smiling and he mouthed the words 'thank you'.

Belle felt tears running down her cheeks. I saved him, she thought and inside her there was a silent cry. Goodbye

Aleksy, for ever. Then she grabbed Joe's hand and ran out of the glass doors into the palace gardens to where the trees edged the park.

'This is the way through,' she said as they ran. 'Look at the trees. Can you see that they're changing?'

'They're our old trees from the park,' said Joe, 'and there's a smell, sort of dusty, that I remember. It's London isn't it?'

Belle could just hear the sound of traffic as she and Joe stepped into a summer evening in Tavistock Square. The beautiful Viennese court clothes were gone and they were dressed as before, like London children in 1944.

They walked back along the well-known pavements. As they opened the shop door the little clock struck the half hour. It was half past ten and Belle's note was still on the table.

13

BACK AT THE SHOP

IT WAS SO STRANGE BEING BACK IN THE SHOP. For the next few weeks it was like living in two worlds. Part of her still seemed to be in Vienna. Belle could hear the music from the little orchestra in the palace ball room and feel the soft silk and velvet of her lovely clothes. She built wonderful dreams about how she might meet Aleksy again one day.

For much of the time she sat on her own, reading books from the library and waiting for customers. Joe had started at a school round the corner and she'd been offered a place at Upper School, but wasn't sorry to find that she couldn't start until next term because of bomb damage to some of the classrooms. Uncle Griff was out for much of the day.

'Where does he go?' Joe asked, but Belle wasn't sure. She knew that he did some war work as a telephone operator and he helped down at Victoria Station on the Salvation Army post, welcoming soldiers off the trains. But on some rainy days he would come back quite late with his coat and shoes wet and muddy, as if he had been walking for hours.

She shook her head. 'He has bad days sometimes, I think.'

'Yes I know,' said Joe. 'It's when he comes back to the shop and tries to sound cheerful but it doesn't really sound like him and he doesn't ask about the shop or want to play a game of chess or anything. He just goes up to his room.'

'I think he's worried about money.'

'Hasn't he got enough?'

'Well you know he told us about the repairs and the rates for the shop? There are hardly any customers and almost no money coming in. Now he's got us to feed as well and when I went down for the bread, the grumpy old woman in the grocery asked me when we'd be paying what we owed.'

'What did you tell her?'

'Oh I just said "soon" and walked out quickly. Perhaps it's just because it's the end of the month and he hasn't been paid yet.'

But Joe wasn't really listening.

'I think we could get some more money, Belle. You know Uncle Griff's friend, old Zeb who has the bookstall at the market? He asked me if I wanted to give him a hand on Saturdays, but I've had an even better idea. As well as helping him, I could set up my own stall next to his and take some of the cheap tin toys, you know the ones that are just copies of the old ones? People would buy them for presents for their children. I thought I could take Meffy with me, not to sell of course, but he'd play his lute and bring everyone to the stall.'

'That's a brilliant idea! There are still lots of the clockwork toys in the boxes and children don't come into the shop, so we're never going to sell them here.' Belle remembered an idea she'd had herself when they were first cleaning up the shop.

'There's still the back room free, remember? We could do it up and take in a lodger, perhaps a soldier on leave. Do you think Uncle Griff would be OK with that?'

'Why not? Sounds good to me. Let's ask him this evening.'

'So you think it's time you went out to work, do you?' Uncle Griff joked. 'There must be plenty of tall chimneys in London waiting to be cleaned. Do you fancy going up a chimney as a little sweep?'

'Oh do be serious,' Belle muttered to herself. Sometimes she found Uncle Griff's jokes really annoying.

'We thought you might be a bit short of money,' she blurted out.

Uncle Griff ran his fingers through his dark hair and she noticed that there were silver streaks. He looked older and tired. 'Well you could just be right, old girl,' he said. 'The money isn't exactly flowing in, and I've got some blighters after me for repayment, but don't worry we'll pull through.'

He turned back to Joe and his voice didn't sound jokey any more.

'Well done old chap. The market stall could certainly be a runner for the weekends. I know old Zeb could do with a hand and he'd be pleased to have you around.'

81

He thought for a bit. 'A lodger's not a bad idea either. I think the army pays quite reasonable rent. Some of those poor lads come back to nothing, poor little beggars. I've seen them come off the train with nobody waiting for them. They're from the Polish Free Army, brave chaps. They've escaped the Nazis and the Russians and now they're fighting with the British army.'

He slapped his hand down on the table. 'Yes, in fact that's a damn good idea. I'm down at Victoria Station tomorrow. Do you fancy coming with me Belle, while young Joe's at school?'

So next morning Belle set off with Uncle Griff. She felt slightly nervous sitting at the Salvation Army desk at Victoria. As the trains pulled into the station she saw lines of young men hanging out of the windows, searching for loved ones on the platform. They looked so tired and many of them had bandages or crutches. There were tears as they hugged their families. But for the line of soldiers quietly queuing up at the Salvation Army desk there were no families, no welcome back, and no home.

Belle sat next to Uncle Griff. 'Name? Regiment? Length of leave?' He asked, and Belle carefully filled in the forms. Then suddenly her heart leapt. She saw a tall young soldier with an injured leg walking slowly and stiffly towards them. Was it something about the way he held his head that she recognised?

'Can we help you?' she said softly. 'What is your name?' The young man looked at her, and Belle's heart calmed down. No he wasn't Aleksy, of course he wasn't. The face was quite different but the eyes were grey-blue, like his.

'My name is Janek Borski,' he replied.

'Where will you be staying in London?' asked Uncle Griff, as Belle filled in the form.

'I do not have accommodation in London,' said the young man. 'I must report my unit.' He pointed to his leg and shrugged. 'Perhaps cannot return to fight.'

Uncle Griff looked at Belle who nodded.

'You must report to your unit first,' he said, 'but, if they recommend extended leave in London, we may be able to help with accommodation. Here's my card. We have a spare room and would be pleased to welcome you there.'

So that was how Janek came to stay at the shop.

He arrived the same evening with his kit bag, and stared with delight at the mechanical marvels on the shelves.

'They are wonderful,' he said, seeing Uncle Griff at work at his table with cogs and wheels spread out in front of him.

'But I help? My father and grandfather clockmakers in Poland.'

'Well that is very handy, old chap, I could do with a bit of help,' said Uncle Griff.

Janek's leg had been badly damaged by a grenade and when his appointment with the army doctor came up he was told that he was unlikely to be able to return to the front.

'All my comrades are fighting there,' he told Belle when he came back dejected from the hospital. How can I stay here when they lose their lives?' He was trying to put on a brave face, but Belle could see that he was holding back tears. *He's so far away from home and who knows when he'll be able to go back.*

'Will you tell me about your country,' she said, remembering how Aleksy loved to talk about Poland.

Janek gave a tight little smile. 'My country, my poor country, what is to tell? Warsaw, our beautiful city, is occupied now by Germans for five years. But Polish people are brave. They will not give up. There is resistance movement.' He stopped for a moment. 'My two brothers fighting there, underground in Warsaw.' He shrugged his shoulders. 'I do not hear from them, of course, but I hope. What else but hope?'

Janek fitted easily into their lives at the shop. He was a natural craftsman and enjoyed helping Uncle Griff mend the mechanical figures. He carved little models out of any pieces of wood that he could find and Joe put these on his Saturday market stall which was going well. Meffy, the old devil, played his lute and always drew a crowd. The little mechanical toys sold much better there than they did in the shop.

'Do you think we're doing OK now?' Joe asked Belle one Saturday after he'd proudly handed his day's takings to Uncle Griff.

Belle smiled. 'I don't know how much money he still owes to that "blighter", as he calls him, and he's still worried about all the repairs that have to be done to the shop, but things do seem better don't they? The woman at the grocery isn't quite as grumpy when I ask for things on tick, so he must have paid some bills. I just wish we could do something really splendid,' she laughed, 'you know, find a treasure or something, like they do in books.'

There was movement from the shelves and jingly music as the instruments started up by themselves. Belle was used to them now. They were the background to life in the shop.

'The mechanicals seem to know something. Perhaps they're telling us that we will find treasure one day. Hey, Joe, the snake charmer's looking straight at us!'

The Indian boy was playing his pipe, swaying gently as the lid of his basket lifted.

'Where's the snake? It usually comes out by now,' said Joe. 'Look there's something shiny in the basket.'

As Joe reached out to pick up the snake charmer, the pipe music stopped and the lid of the basket closed.

He turned the key, and the mechanism started up again, but the eyes were now just the blank eyes of an automaton. Joe had a good look inside the basket.

'There's nothing in there now, but I'm sure there was something. It looked like a star. Did you see it?'

'I saw something shiny, and I was thinking of treasure, but it could have been a star.'

Joe put the Indian boy carefully back on the shelf. 'There's a star sometimes in my dreams, a beautiful star in the sky and Kadir points to it. Do you think it means something special?'

'I think it might,' said Belle. 'I often feel the mechanicals are trying to tell us something but I just wish we could understand them better.'

14

THE STAR

'Do they ever do any teaching at that school of yours, young Joe?' asked Uncle Griff as Joe arrived back at the shop one afternoon covered in dust with a canvas bag on his shoulder.

'Mr Grimley says finding out for yourself is better,' grinned Joe. 'We're making a museum at school and he wants us to bring stuff in. I went to that little church by the corner of Duke Street. You know the one, St Anthony's? A bomb went through the roof and it's not being used now, but the vicar saw me in the church yard and he said I could have a look around, as long as I asked him before taking anything. See, this is what I found.'

He tipped some pieces of coloured glass onto the table, shattered fragments from a stained-glass window. 'They managed to take out most of the windows from the church and store them safely before the bomb dropped, but this little window was too high up in the roof. It's really sad it got smashed.'

'Yes, is sad.' Janek walked over to the table and started to fit some of the pieces together to make a pattern. 'I have some wood. Perhaps I make frame? When light shines through will be like a window again.'

'Yeah, that'd be great. Can we start now?'

'Some work to be done first, old chap,' said Uncle Griff. 'Talking of windows, Janek, we need to fix those blackout boards in your room. They're letting out light and we don't want to give those damn bombers a target.'

Joe picked up the fragments of glass one by one, rubbing off the dust on the sleeve of his sweater and holding each one up to the light. They made splashes of wonderful rich colours, deep sea blue, blood red, and sunshine yellow.

'Oh they're beautiful,' said Belle. 'Like jewels.'

She watched as Joe laid the fragments out on the table, working out from the centre to form the points of a roughly made star. 'What do you think?' he asked.

'They're lovely. They almost seem to have their own light.'

It was true the colours were glowing with a brightness which now seemed to be filling the whole room.

'Look Joe. Look up at the ceiling!'

Patches of brightly coloured light were swirling around in a circle and cascading down the walls in a wonderful magical light show. As they watched, the colours formed themselves into one shining, multi-coloured star which covered the whole ceiling, turning slowly in constantly changing patterns.

It was exciting, beautiful, breath-taking and Belle and Joe just stood there with their heads thrown back, staring up at the endlessly changing flow of magic light.

The music Belle could hear was soft, tinkling, like an orchestra of musical-boxes and it took her a while to realise that it came from the characters on the shelves, playing their instruments.

'Listen. They are actually telling us something.' They both moved closer to the shelves.

'Find the star. Find the star. You must look for the star.' It was whispered over and over again by a chorus of tiny voices.

'Which star? What do you mean?' But they received no answer. As if the clockwork was running down, the movement gradually slowed to a halt, the whispering stopped and, when Belle turned back to look again at the ceiling, the magical, coloured star had disappeared.

'What did they mean, find the star? Did they mean that lovely star on the ceiling?'

Joe shrugged. 'I don't know where it came from. Perhaps it was just a trick of the light.' The little pieces of glass on the table looked very ordinary now. He shuffled them with his hand. 'I don't see how it can have been made by these scraps.'

'Can you talk to the mechanicals and ask them what they mean?'

Joe shook his head. 'I'm not really any closer to them than you are. I can feel when they're upset or excited. But I can't actually talk to them.' There was a pause. 'Well, except perhaps Meffy. I think perhaps I could ask him.'

'Come on then,' said Belle, turning back to the shelves.

Mephisto was standing with his lute in his hands, staring vacantly in front of him. He looked like nothing more than a clockwork toy and Belle's excited feeling disappeared. I don't think he can tell us anything, she thought. But Joe didn't seem discouraged.

'Meffy,' he whispered, 'Meffy, what's all this about a star? We don't understand. How can we look for a star?'

There was a slight movement of Mephisto's arm and Belle heard the lute start up with its familiar little tune. The automaton's eyes flipped open and shut and his mouth moved jerkily as his head turned from side to side with the music. Joe must have turned the key. Is that all? We're not going to learn much here.

As the music slowed down Mephisto gave his usual low bow. Then, holding his lute in one hand, he looked straight at them and with an elegant gesture reached out his right arm, clearly asking them to look behind them.

They turned round together. Wow, look at that! Belle laughed out loud with excitement. The shop had disappeared and they were standing in a court yard decorated with little trees in pots and a gently splashing fountain. In front of them was a stone building, like an old church, with a row of pillars along one wall and on the carved arch above the door were the words: *Spring Gardens.*

She grabbed Joe's hand and pulled him forward. 'We're travelling again, but where are we this time?' She looked round at the crowded courtyard. 'Something special's going on by the look of things.'

A queue had formed by the door of the stone building and the courtyard was buzzing with chatter from groups of men, women and children, all dressed for a day out; long flowing dresses for the women, with pretty shawls and wide hats. The little girls were dressed almost exactly like their mothers and the boys looked very smart in breeches and jackets to match their fathers

A small gang of ragged boys ran from group to group, begging for money from the crowd and a girl of about Belle's age came up to them pushing a little wooden cart. 'Buy a Seville orange, Miss?

'Oh I'd love an orange. Have we got any money?' Joe had turned his pockets inside out and was shaking his head. 'Nope, nothing here.' The girl shrugged her shoulders and moved on calling out to the crowd 'Fine Seville oranges, fine lemons, fine...'

'See the amazin' golden peacock clock, and other mechanical wonders of the Orient. Only half a guinea, tickets half a guinea.' A lanky young man was striding up and down, ringing his bell and shouting above the noise of the crowd.

'We're still in London, aren't we? It looks like quite a long time ago. What's your guess, Joe?'

'I've no idea where we are, but old Meffy certainly knew something and he sent us here to find out. Do you think we can go into the exhibition? There's a man at the door so we'll have to get past him 'cos we haven't got any money. Let's give it a try.'

They joined the queue, staying close to a family with children of about the same age and, when the man was looking down to count the tickets, slipped quickly behind the group and walked into the hall.

Joe gave a soft whistle. 'Wow, Uncle Griff should see this.'

In a glass case almost as high as the ceiling, a peacock made of gold was standing on the outstretched branches of an oak tree. A tinkle of bells chimed the hour just as the children came in and the peacock lifted his magnificent tail to its full height, turning slowly, to show off his fan of golden feathers, as other small golden creatures scampered through the branches of the tree.

In front of them stood an enormous model of an elephant, sparkling with precious stones and next to it a life-sized figure of a boy with a pineapple on his head, which burst open as the clock chimed to show a nest of little birds.

Belle laughed, 'Joe, that boy looks like you.'

'Except you wouldn't catch me wearing a pineapple on my head.'

'These are incredible aren't they?' she breathed. 'They make our mechanical toys look really ordinary.'

'Not half! Just look round the room. There are loads more!'

He was pointing upwards. 'Hey up there, see, it's like our star.'

She looked up at the dark red painted ceiling. The pattern of moving light cascading across it was just like the one in the shop that afternoon. 'But where's it coming from?'

Joe had already moved towards a table in the centre of the room. 'Here it is. Hey, this must be our star. Come and look!'

It was one of the most beautiful things she had ever seen; a miracle of glass, tiny silver mirrors, and sparkling stones, fashioned into a series of stars, which circled and spiralled one above the other, picking up the light from the chandeliers and sending it spinning in rainbow swirls across the walls and ceiling.

Joe reached out to touch and felt a heavy hand on his shoulder. 'No touching, young sir. May I see your ticket please?'

He pretended to feel in his pockets. 'Oh I'm sorry I must have dropped it.' He looked at Belle for help.

'Yes, when you fell over outside. We'd better go and look for it,' she said, grabbing him by the arm and heading for the door. 'Quick! Make a run for it!'

She could hear the man calling after them as they pelted down the steps and across the courtyard. She'd spotted a small iron gate in the corner but as they rushed up to it she saw that it was shut. Panic, where to now? She turned round to ask Joe, crashed straight into something very hard, and went flying.

'Hey what's going on?' It was Uncle Griff's voice. Belle was sitting on the floor of the shop next to the heavy wooden table. She had run straight into it and was nursing a bruised shin.

'Are you all right old girl? Steady on there.' He gave Belle a hand to help her up and caught sight of the catalogue lying open on the floor. 'I say, what's this?

'My goodness where did you find it? James Cox's old catalogue. In with all those old magazines, was it? Well I never. This is a pretty rare item.'

Belle looked at the book in Uncle Griff's hands. No longer the smart catalogue she had picked up in the exhibition, the blue cover was faded and patchy, and the pages curled and brown at the edges. On the front page in stylish letters, she read: *Mr Cox's Museum, Spring Gardens, London, 1772.*

So that's where we were!

Uncle Griff sat down at the table, excitedly flipping through the pages. 'Just listen to this: *Life-sized copper figure of a gardener's boy wearing a hat that concealed musical chimes and covered with a silver-gilt pineapple.* By Golly, old James Cox! What a master he was, there's never been anyone like him since.'

Belle and Joe were peering over his shoulder and Belle gave Joe a secret smile.

'Where are all those lovely things now?' she asked.

'Ah well, poor old Cox. He made his money selling these exquisite pieces abroad to the Imperial palaces in China and the Maharajas in India, who just loved them. He was doing very well but then the British government put a heavy tax on luxury exports so he couldn't send them abroad anymore and he had to sell them all off.

'He put on a splendid exhibition. I think this catalogue must have come from there. It was very popular, apparently, but people came to look rather than to buy, so in the end Cox held a lottery and got rid of them all that way. A few ended up in museums. The lovely peacock clock is

in Russia I believe, but most of them just disappeared...
could be anywhere.'

Belle knew what Joe was thinking. What had happened
to the star? As soon as Uncle Griff left the room she
picked up the catalogue and started to leaf through it page
by page.

'Here it is,' she called out. *'Item 125: The Maharaja's star;
the piece being a mechanical star decorated with 3000 precious stones in
spiral and circular motion.'* She could see it again in her mind,
the beauty of the swirling sparkling light.

Joe walked over to the shelves where Mephisto was
bending over his lute. 'Well Meffy, we found the star, and
we know it was in the exhibition. But how can we find
where it is now?' The old devil's face stared back at him
blankly, his mouth slightly open. There was no sound or
movement from the mechanicals.

15

THE BARON COMES BACK

SOMETHING WAS GOING TO HAPPEN. BELLE knew it. She was on her own, looking after the shop a few days later. The mechanicals were going crazy on the shelves. The acrobats were summersaulting, the drummer boy was banging his drum and the little dancer was pirouetting round and round as if she would never stop.

She bent over the shelves. 'What is it? Tell me, please?' she begged them, even though she knew she wouldn't get an answer.

There was a slight sound behind her and she spun round. She hadn't heard the door open or the sound of the monkey cymbals but she recognised the tall figure, the long grey coat, the click of boots brought neatly together and the brief formal bow.

'Ah Miss Carrington, it is good to see you again.'

'Baron von Kempelen!' She was so excited that she nearly grabbed hold of his arm but then she remembered his very formal manners and stepped back, politely holding out her hand which he took in his. It felt cold and damp, like a fish, and she took her hand away as quickly as she could.

He looked so much older. He still wore his hair rather long but there was less of it now and it had turned quite white. His face was even thinner than before, and his dark eyes seemed to have sunk deeper behind his high cheek bones. A lot of time must have passed in his world.

'Oh I am so glad you've come back. There's so much I want to ask you. We left Vienna in a great rush, didn't we? Tell me please. What happened in the games with the Turkish chessmaster, did he keep on winning? Was the Empress pleased? And Captain Aleksy, did he go back to Poland?'

'Ah the chessmaster... not all went well, I am afraid. That is a story I have to tell you and your brother and it is the reason I am here. But the handsome Polish Captain? Yes he returned to his beloved Poland and I heard that he was the leader of several further insurrections. He became quite a hero to his people I believe.'

Yes of course he was a hero, he was so brave. There was a sharp pain in her chest. Oh Aleksy!

The Baron was still talking.

'But here, I have something for you and your brother. The Captain asked me to give it to you, but I have had to keep it for a very long time.'

He took out of his pocket an old and dog-eared card. A tarnished regimental button was sewn onto the corner.

'From him?' Belle gasped.

The writing was small and faded but she managed to read it. *To the two brave children who saved my life, my wishes for long and happy lives in their own country.*

It was signed Captain Aleksy Worousky, 1st Division, Polish Guards.

In bold letters, printed on the card were the words. POLAND WILL BE FREE

Belle turned away as she felt the blood rush to her face. How amazing. So he did think of us.

Just at that moment Joe ran into the room and stopped suddenly as he saw the Baron. 'I knew something had happened. I could hear the mechanicals making such a fuss.'

Belle realised that she hadn't been very polite to their guest. She passed the card to Joe.

'Please do sit down Baron and I will bring some tea. We want to hear all about the chessmaster.'

'I have need of your good services again,' she heard the Baron say to Joe as she came back with the tea tray.

'You must understand that my Turkish chessmaster was sensationally popular in Vienna and I am glad to say that we had no more unpleasant incidents such the one with the mad young count.'

He turned to Belle and gave her a brief smile, recognising the role she had played.

'Because of this success, there was so much interest from abroad in his remarkable achievements that I was encouraged by the Empress Maria Theresa to make a tour of Europe, and we visited your own beautiful city of London. The crowds flocked to every performance. It was gratifying of course, but I confess that I grew tired of being merely a travelling showman, and had just decided to return to Vienna when I received a request that I could not refuse.'

'Oh no, you didn't sell the Turk did you?' asked Joe.

'As I said, it was a request I could not refuse from King Frederick the Great of Prussia. He was a keen chess player and had heard of my automaton's reputation so he sent me an invitation to play at his court. We packed up again and travelled to Berlin.' The Baron paused and frowned, 'unfortunately, however, this turned out to be a bad move for the Turk.'

'Why? What happened?'

'I will explain. King Frederick was so excited by the automaton's performance that he wanted to discover its secret. So, as he was one of the wealthiest monarchs in Europe, he simply offered to buy it for an enormous sum, in order that he could examine it himself.' The Baron shrugged his shoulders ruefully. 'I could not say no, but of course he was not pleased when he discovered that he had been fooled by a simple conjuring trick. He never told anyone the secret, but he ordered the automaton to be packed up and consigned to an obscure corner of the palace and I never saw it again.'

'Oh how sad!' Belle murmured.

'Well, I was busy. I had many engineering duties to perform at court. I was pleased with the reputation the automaton had earned. People were still talking about it with admiration and I was confident that it would be remembered by future generations. So I was not unhappy to let it go.' His dark eyes clouded with anger. 'But now all these years later, what do I hear? That my wonderful chess-playing automaton was found in an old cellar and has been bought by some fool of a German toymaker, who has repaired it and now has the effrontery to claim the invention as his own!'

Joe jumped up. 'The rotten cheat, how dare he?'

The Baron shook his head. 'My main concern,' he went on, 'is the fact that this man Maelzel is a fool, and may ruin the chessmaster's reputation for ever. So,' he turned to them both, 'that is why I am asking you to accompany me back to Vienna. There is a very important game which I would ask Joe to play.'

Joe's face was glowing with excitement.

'Oh yes. I've been practising my game, especially the openings, and Aleksy showed me how the mechanism all works. I am sure I could play. But what about the Kadir, the spirit. What happened to him? Did you see him again?'

'Kadir played many games for me, while the chessmaster was touring Europe. I don't believe he was ever beaten, but I have not seen him since the automaton was thrown into King Frederick's cellar. I had promised him his freedom but,' he shrugged, 'it was not a promise that I could keep. He is still tied in some way to the automaton, but I do not think he will play chess for that fool Maelzel.'

He rose slowly from his chair. 'So, my young friends, will you come with me again?'

Belle looked at Joe who nodded enthusiastically.

'Ah, good,' the Baron started moving towards the door. 'Shall we go then? There are certain things that I will need to explain to you on the way.'

Just as they were leaving, Janek came into the room. He stopped when he saw the Baron but then noticed the card in Joe's hand and gave a cry of surprise.

Belle stepped forward to introduce them. 'Janek, this is one of our customers, Mr Kempel.' She had to think quickly. 'He is interested in army regalia from the eighteenth century.'

Janek seemed quite upset. 'But please may I see it? I see the name, Captain Aleksy Worousky. Is important for me. He is my ancestor. He is Polish hero.'

Belle stopped where she was and stared at Janek. Aleksy is his ancestor? Of course I knew there had to be a connection. I just knew it.

The Baron was by the door and anxious to leave. He bowed politely. 'I am very pleased to meet you, young man. How interesting that Captain Worousky was your ancestor. Now we have an important visit to make. Miss Carrington will be able to tell you all about it when she returns.'

Janek just stood there looking puzzled and rather worried.

'Please tell my uncle that we will be back very soon,' said Belle, although she didn't want to leave Janek like that. She gave a little tug to the regimental button, broke the slender thread holding it to the card and pressed the button into Janek's hand.

'Here,' she whispered. 'You should have it. This is for you. One day I will tell you a story I know about your ancestor. He was a real hero wasn't he?'

Janek stared at the button in his hand. 'Thank you, thank you,' he murmured. 'This is very special for me.' Belle smiled at him happily. Suddenly Aleksy seemed quite close again. She ran off to catch up with Joe and the Baron.

16

VIENNA AGAIN

IN FRONT OF HER THE BARON WAS WALKING towards the park, with Joe beside him. Back to Vienna! The thought gave her a delicious thrill of excitement as she followed the two of them through the trees. As before the scene changed gradually. This time she followed it more closely. First the temperature dropped and the air felt colder and fresher, then new smells crept in; the smell of fresh horse dung from the carriages, a faint spicy smell from the cakes being baked in the kitchens. There was a different sound too, water splashing from a fountain. Finally the trees cleared and she saw again the beautiful Schönbrunn Palace gardens, with their ornamental flower beds and carefully trimmed trees laid out in front of the palace.

Belle looked down at her clothes and gasped with pleasure. This was a new style. The mulberry red coat she was wearing was buttoned tight under her bust and then flowed down to her ankles. Underneath she could see the soft material of her dress, which was white and embroidered with small flowers and leaves.

'Hey Belle, I like your bonnet,' she heard Joe say.

Belle reached up and undid the ribbons. It was a straw bonnet, with a wide brim decorated with red ribbons, little white flowers and a small bunch of cherries.

'Look at me,' said Joe. He was dressed in military costume, with high black boots fitted over white trousers and a splendid dark blue and white military jacket trimmed with gold braid.

She was taken by surprise. He didn't look like her little brother any more.

'Joe, you look really grown up,' she said.

'Everyone seems to be wearing uniform,' said Joe.

Sure enough the park was full of soldiers. Many of them seemed to be off-duty and were strolling through the gardens arm in arm with elegantly dressed ladies. A group passed close to them chatting quietly to each other.

They're speaking French, thought Belle, That's odd. We're in Austria. But which year are we in? She could see from the costumes that it was later than their last visit. The ladies dresses with their high waists reminded her of a picture she had seen. Was it the Emperor Napoleon's time?

Joe had wandered off.

'Hey Belle, come and look. This wasn't here before, was it? It's amazing.'

He was looking at a splendid fountain on the edge of the ornamental lake. Water cascaded down rocky cliffs around statues of sea nymphs and dolphins. Above them was a statue of Neptune in a shell shaped carriage which was being drawn by sea-horses. Water gushed into the lake from every direction, from the shells carried by the sea nymphs, from the mouths of the sea creatures and from the rocky seascape.

'So you are admiring my fountain?' They heard a voice behind them. The Baron had reappeared.

'Your fountain? It's wonderful.'

'Yes indeed, my fountain. It was I who designed a hydraulic system to power all the fountains in the park when I was chief engineer at the court.'

The sun was now low in the sky and the golden evening light danced on the water of the lake. 'Beautiful Vienna,' murmured Belle.

'Come,' said the Baron, 'we cannot stay here long. I have something I must show you.'

They left the palace and walked through the narrow back streets of Vienna until they came to a small churchyard. There was still just enough light in the dusky sky to make out several rows of gravestones set among the small bushes and trees. The Baron stopped beside one of the stones, and bent to rub the moss from the letters.

'Here,' he said.

Belle knelt down to read the inscription.

Wolfgang Von Kempelen, died March 26, 1804

She drew in her breath sharply and looked up at the Baron's face. He was standing with the faint evening light behind him. The dark pools of his eyes seemed to have sunk deeper than ever into the boney structure of his pale face and she shuddered at the recognition. I am looking at the skull of a dead man.

She tried to make her voice sound calm and matter of fact. 'It says that you died in 1804. How long ago was that?'

'It is nine years since my body was buried here. My own time has passed. But there is more to read.' He bent down to rub the remaining moss from the inscription. 'Now, how good is your Latin? These are the words of the Roman poet Horace.'

Non omnis moriar, read Belle.

'What does it mean?' asked Joe.

She struggled to remember the Latin she'd learnt at school. '*Moriar* means *die* or *dead* I think and *omnis* means *all* so *non omnis* must mean *not all*. *Not all dead? Not completely dead?*' She looked up at the Baron. 'Is that it? You are dead, but not completely dead?'

A slight smile appeared on the Baron's lips. The light had changed, the image of the skull had faded and he looked more like the Baron she knew. He held Belle's gaze for a moment. 'Well done, little scholar, yes that is just what it means. My body does indeed lie in the grave under that tombstone. But as you can see I am not completely dead.'

Joe had come closer and was listening carefully as the Baron went on. 'You need to understand that some of us are only loosely planted within time. Sometimes we are called Time Travellers. We can find doors that lead through in either direction to the past or the future. So I can sometimes bring you with me on my journeys, but I cannot myself change what has already happened and that is why I need you. I cannot do more here now. I would still be recognised in Vienna. There is an important game for Jozef to play and it is for you to preserve the reputation of the Turkish chessmaster.' There was some urgency in his voice now as if he was in a hurry. 'Here is a letter of introduction. Go to the tavern, Gasthaus Fink. A carriage is waiting at the gate to take you there. Go now!'

'But I don't understand,' said Joe. 'What have we got to do? Please don't go yet.' But the Baron was fading away in the dusk. They could just make out the shadowy form of a figure by the grave and then it disappeared completely.

'We're on our own, Joe,' said Belle.

17

GASTHAUS FINK

Sure enough, Belle and Joe found a carriage waiting for them by the cemetery gate which drove them through the dark, narrow streets to a brightly lit tavern. They could hear laughter and loud voices from inside.

As they opened the door they were hit by a blast of warm air that smelled of hot food and sweaty men. The tavern was crowded, groups of men talking and drinking at all the tables. Waiters in long aprons were dashing about carrying trays with large tankards of beer.

A boy about Joe's age sat at a table in the corner playing chess on his own. He looked up as they came in and Joe went over to show him the letter.

'We're to give this to Herr Maelzel, do you know him?'

'Ol' Maelzel? Yeah, over there on the table under the window. That's my dad with 'im, the fat one.'

Belle saw two men at the table. One was small and well dressed. He had a sulky expression, straggly brown hair and a droopy moustache. The other had a huge belly and a round head that seemed be stuck onto his enormous frame without the help of a neck.

'Herr Maelzel?' said Belle.

The large man looked up suspiciously, grabbed the letter and waved his hand as if to push the children away, but the smaller man reached out for the letter. 'Give it to me Schmidt,' he said. Then, turning to the children, 'I am Herr Maelzel and who is this letter from, Fraulein?'

'It's explained in the letter,' said Belle nervously, having no idea what the letter was about.

Herr Maelzel read the letter carefully, while they waited, and then passed it on without comment to the man he called Schmidt. His eyes narrowed slightly in his rabbity face as he looked at Joe.

'So, I understand that you are something of a chess player, young man,' he said.

The big man gave a grunt of contempt, clearly unimpressed. 'But they're only kids, mein Herr. They could ruin everything.'

'They come with very high recommendation from an influential source,' said Maelzel, and the corner of his mouth turned up slightly, the nearest, Belle thought, that he might ever get to a smile. 'And,' he continued in a lowered voice to Schmidt, 'the boy is the right size, isn't he?'

He's thinking of size of the cabinet, thought Belle. Joe would fit. So they do want him to play the chessmaster's game.

The little man continued in his squeaky, self-important voice.

'My colleague Herr Schmidt and I are engaged in a very important project, one which will have considerable influence, not only in Vienna but throughout Europe. It has been suggested in this letter that you, young man, might be of assistance to us. If you will accompany me, I will explain what is involved.'

Herr Schmidt was still grunting and obviously not impressed, but Maelzel got up from the table.

'Come with me,' he said. 'I have something to show you.'

They followed the two men to a room at the back of the tavern. A pungent smell of rotting rubbish hit them as they went down the steps and Belle brushed aside the spiders' webs hanging from the low ceiling. 'Yuck,' she said. But in spite of the gloomy surroundings she felt a tingle of excitement. Are we going to see the chessmaster again?

A large square object was hidden under a pile of rugs and she knew immediately it was him.

'This,' said Maelzel proudly, as he pulled off the rugs, 'is my spectacular invention. 'An automaton that plays chess.'

There he was! It was their chessmaster, but looking sadly different. The robes and turban were new, made of cheap red material which was much too shiny and some sparkly glass jewels had been added. His left arm seemed to have been re-made, and was a different shape, but she was pleased to see that the carved wooden face was unchanged.

It still had the same haughty expression. The glass eyes stared at them without recognition.

Belle felt a wave of sadness and wished suddenly that she could be back in the Vienna they had known before, with the chessmaster in the beautiful Schönbrunn Palace instead of this dirty backroom, and with it came such a sharp pang of loss for Aleksy that her throat felt blocked and she couldn't speak for a few minutes.

Joe was looking at Belle. She could see that he was wondering whether to tell Maelzel that they already knew about the mechanical chessmaster. But how could they explain that they had seen it such a long time ago? She felt so angry with the nasty little man. What an imposter to claim that it was his own invention! She wasn't going to let him get away with it. Carefully she said, 'My brother and I have read about the mechanical chessmaster, but we understood that it was created by Baron von Kempelen for the court of Empress Maria Theresa.'

Maelzel's shifty eyes glinted with anger.

'Von Kempelen was an amateur. Yes, he made the original automaton, but I have completely reconstructed it after I found it rotting away in a cellar. This is a far superior model. I have even included my amazing speech device. Listen…'

He arranged the chessmen on the board in a checkmate move then took the key to the side of the cabinet. Belle and Joe heard the familiar cranking and whirring sound as the mechanism started up. The wooden figure moved his body slightly, and then reached out his arm across the board.

Maelzel leant down, touching something at the back of the cabinet and the carved head nodded three times.

'Checkmate,' said Joe but he was startled to hear a sound coming from the model itself.

'Échec, Échec' it rasped.

'You see?' said Maelzel smugly, 'It actually says "check mate" in French now. This is far superior to the primitive earlier model that you may have heard of. My reputation has already spread through Vienna and I have been offered some prestigious engagements. I plan to tour Europe with the chessmaster.'

Turning to Joe he said, 'I understand that you are a competent chess player and may be able to work for us. But,' his small eyes glared at the boy, 'I will have no nonsense, you understand? You do exactly as you are told and you speak to no one. If you work well, you will be well paid.'

Belle knew that she didn't want to work for such an unpleasant pair. She wished they could just say no and go back to London.

But she could see that Joe was really excited. He knew all about the inner workings of the mechanical model. Aleksy had shown him how to manipulate the magnets that moved the chess pieces and they had played against each other with Joe inside the cabinet. He was just longing to have a go. Besides, the Baron had brought them here for an important assignment. He's got good reason to worry about the chessmaster's reputation with Maelzel in charge, she thought, and we did agree to help. We can't go back on our word now.

She looked at Joe, who nodded his head. 'Yes,' she said, 'my brother will work for you. But he suffers from asthma and is not strong. I will have to be with him.'

She heard Schmidt muttering something under his breath, which sounded like. 'You'll do what you're bleedin' told.' Maelzel gave a curt nod of his head and they left the room.

'Whew, what a charming pair!' Belle walked up to cabinet. 'Oh poor old chessmaster. He looks terrible, doesn't he? But Kadir's not here. The eyes are completely empty. Somehow I feel that he hasn't been here for years.'

Joe shook his head. 'No, no sign of him. But didn't the Baron say that his spirit was still attached to the chessmaster in some way? Perhaps he's around somewhere.' He was stroking the shiny brown wood of the cabinet and he reached up to re-arrange the chessmen on the board. 'I just can't wait to have a game.'

He looked so pleased and excited that Belle decided not to say any more about her dislike of Maelzel and Schmidt. We can always go home if things don't work out, she told herself.

Back in the tavern the children sat down in the corner opposite Herr Schmit's son who told them that his name was Pieter. A waitress brought them a big plate of meat and potatoes and they tucked in hungrily.

Pieter stared at them for a while. His small grey eyes looked wary, as if he would like to talk but couldn't trust strangers. He made Belle think of a puppy she'd known on the Benions' farm, who'd always been badly treated, but still wanted to play. The boy's face was pale and he had a row of angry looking spots across the top of his forehead which he kept reaching up to scratch.

'So that mechanical contraption's gonna play a game with Boney, then?' He blurted out suddenly.

'Boney, who's Boney?' said Joe, with a mouthful of potato.

The boy looked at him as if he was mad. 'Who's Boney? Bonaparte, of course, Na-pol-e-on Bo-na-parte, or ain't you never heard of him?' he said with a sneer.

'Napoleon Bonaparte, yes of course I've heard of him,' said Joe, 'but how can the chessmaster play with him in Vienna?'

''Cos that's where he is, of course, here in Vienna with his Frenchies. Ain't you seen them strutting round the place? They're all livin' in the Schönbrunn palace, stuffin' themselves, the fat frogs.' He spat on the floor, then looked hard at both of them. 'Don't you know nuffin? Where you two from?'

'We've only just arrived in Vienna,' said Belle, wishing she had learnt more about Napoleon. She didn't remember anything about a war with Austria.

'Well Boney gave the mangy ol' Austrian army a good thrashin', didn't he?' said Pieter. 'He's callin' himself Emperor now. You should see him marching about the town. "Like a dog on its hind legs" my dad says.'

'But what about the mechanical chessmaster?' asked Joe. 'Have you seen it play a game yet?'

'Yeah, my dad wanted me to play, but old Maelzel says I'm not good enough.' He gave Joe another long hard look. 'So are you playin'?'

'I guess so,' said Joe. 'I'm sorry if you wanted to play.'

The boy laughed. 'Nah, I didn't wanna play. I'm good mind you, but not that good. Anyways, I know the only reason as my dad tried to get me into the cabinet was 'cos of the star.'

The Star? Belle caught Joe's eye. She felt a buzz of excitement.

'What do you mean, the star?' asked Joe.

Pieter put one finger against the side of his nose and leant across the table to Joe, as if to tell him an important secret.

'Ain't you never heard about the star? They say that the man what made the chessmaster drove a hard bargain and were paid a fortune for it by old King Fred, the German, what left it to rot in 'is cellars.'

'Yes we do know about that,' said Joe. 'It was Baron von Kempelen, the man who invented the chessmaster and sold it to King Frederick, wasn't it?'

Pieter bent down even closer 'Well what them's sayin' is this, that the old man, the inventor, he asked for a beautiful mechanical star, what belonged to the German king; at least 3000 precious stones in it, worth a fortune it seems, and the old king gave it to him 'cos he wanted the chessmaster that bad.'

'But...' he paused dramatically and looked up at Belle. 'Nobody ain't never seen it since.'

Again a flash of understanding passed between Belle and Joe. The Baron had once owned the Maharaja's star. A jigsaw piece seemed to slip into place.

'You mean it just disappeared?' asked Joe.

'Well the old inventor's dead now 'course, but people say the secret of the star's wiv the chessmaster. My dad thought it was likely hidden in the cabinet somewhere, so he said he would help old Maelzel repair it.

There was a look of glee on Pieter's skinny little face, as if he was about to burst into laughter. 'Only he ain't found nothin'!'

Belle looked up to see the burly figure of Schmidt looming over them.

'What you talking about, you stupid boy?' he said, aiming a blow at Pieter which he ducked expertly. 'Didn't I just tell you to keep your mouth shut? Make yourself useful and get me another beer.'

'And you,' he turned to Belle and Joe, 'get up to your room. We'll see you sharp at eight, Jozef, to see how you shape up, so no lying about in bed.'

They went up to a little room on the top floor and looked out of the narrow window onto the rooftops of Vienna.

'It was the Maharaja's star that Pieter was talking about wasn't it? The one we saw in Cox's museum, that Meffy and the others told us we had to find. But the Baron never said anything about it.'

'He did tell us he'd been offered a price that he couldn't refuse by King Frederick. Perhaps it was the star? In any case it seems well and truly lost now. The whole thing was left in the cellars for years, anyone could have taken it. Schmidt would certainly have found it if it was in the chessmaster.'

'I suppose so, but I can't help feeling there's more to it than that.' She climbed into the small hard bed and pulled the blanket up to her chin.

'This isn't like last time, is it?' she said, thinking of the lovely soft feather beds in the oak-panelled bedroom of their old house in Vienna.

'No, but I do get to play chess inside the chessmaster this time,' said Joe. 'I really wanted to do that.'

'It actually looks as if you might be playing against Napoleon himself,' said Belle. 'You know Uncle Griff told us that the chessmaster did play Napoleon once?'

'Did he win?' asked Joe.

'I can't remember,' said Belle. 'Oh bother, we should have paid more attention.'

Joe sounded worried. 'I hope Napoleon's not too good. There might be trouble if I lose.'

'Don't worry,' said Belle sleepily. 'I should think he's been too busy conquering the whole of Europe to have much time left for playing games of chess.'

18

FRENCH SPIES

In the morning they were woken by church bells and the smell of freshly baked bread.

They dressed quickly and went down to the tavern, which was already crowded and noisy.

Herr Schmidt was sitting by himself with a large tankard of beer in front of him. He looked up as they came in, but his heavy, round face showed no flicker of a welcome. When they'd finished eating, Belle heard him push his chair away from the table and smelled his beery breath as he stood behind her.

'Come on then, Herr Maelzel's waiting for you,' he said roughly, completely ignoring Belle, and took Joe off with him into the room at the back of the tavern.

She didn't see Joe again until the middle of the day, when he came back into the tavern on his own, hot and red in the face but grinning with excitement.

'It's just the same inside as it was before,' he whispered. 'Maelzel hasn't changed it at all. The magnets under the chess pieces are all still there, and the same levers and strings to move the chessmaster's hands and his head. There's just one extra lever which you pull to make him say *échec*, but that's all. You can see that the cabinet needed a lot of repair though. It must have been left in the cellar for a long time.'

'How did the chess go?'

Joe grinned. 'It's not too much of a problem beating Maelzel, though he fancies himself as a chess player. But it's really hot inside the cabinet and very dusty, and I get a bit wheezy.'

For the next few days Joe spent his mornings in the back room practising working the machinery in the automaton smoothly. Belle knew he was enjoying himself. She felt restless on her own, and drifted back to the gardens of the Schönbrunn palace, watching the spectacular displays of the fountains, feeding bread to the flocks of geese and ducks on the lake, and looking at the beautiful fashions of the ladies who paraded along the paths.

One morning she noticed a young man who seemed to be looking at her, but when she looked back at him he turned away quickly and moved towards the exit.

He seems to know who I am, thought Belle, puzzled.

So she was not surprised to see the same young man come into the tavern that evening.

He looked around him cautiously before coming up to their table, where he bowed politely and offered them a card. 'My master would like to talk to you,' he said. 'Will you follow me please?'

Joe looked at Belle, who nodded quickly and they walked out into the courtyard of the tavern, where a very grand coach was standing.

'These are the young people, Monsieur le Chevalier,' he said.

A finely dressed gentleman in a large hat leaned out of the carriage window.

'Ah, *bien, bien,* good, good. I apologise for disturbing your meal. Allow me to introduce myself. I am Philippe de Mayard, Chevalier de Montanan. I am pleased to meet you. I believe that you are guests of our good landlord here at the Gasthaus Fink, and you are perhaps involved in the enterprise of the redoubtable chess-playing Turk?'

'They know all about us,' thought Belle, and she answered carefully.

'We are staying here and my brother is employed as an assistant to Herr Maelzel.'

The man nodded. 'You have, I expect, made the acquaintance of Herr Schmidt?'

As the children nodded he carried on talking.

'You will understand, I am sure that not all Austrians have welcomed our Emperor with the enthusiasm of the more sophisticated Viennese citizens. Some are not able to appreciate the advantages of joining our great European Empire.'

He beckoned them closer to the carriage door and lowered his voice.

'We know that in certain circles there is some unrest, even, we believe, possible plans for disruption and we need to know who is leading this. We would be very interested to hear what is being discussed by Herr Schmidt and his friends over their beer in the evenings. You can expect a good reward for any information.'

'You want us to be spies?' exclaimed Joe.

'An ugly word! We wish simply to have ears in various places in Vienna, so that we can assess the situation. We will contact you again.'

With that he made a curt sign to the driver and the carriage moved swiftly away.

'What shall we do, Belle? Schmidt and his mates talk all the time about how they're going to get rid of Napoleon, but I don't think they've got any real plans. They're just full of hate. But Pieter told me that a group of them meet in a different tavern. Perhaps they are conspirators.'

'Well it is their country,' said Belle. 'I'm not surprised that they don't want the French here. But do you notice how all the rich Viennese seem to be quite happy to mix with the French? They're all still riding in their carriages and walking in the Schönbrunn gardens.'

'We're not going to tell that rat-faced Frenchman anything are we?'

'No of course not, well nothing useful anyway, but there is no harm in reporting some of the conversations about rat-catching and winning at cards, and where to get the best sausages, just to keep him happy.'

Joe laughed, 'Yeah that sounds just like them. We could make up a whole conversation without giving away anything useful to that snoopy French count at all.'

Next day brought exciting news. Joe came running up to their room. His face was pink and sweaty, his hair was sticking up on end, and he was bursting with news.

'It's him, Napoleon himself. I'm going to play a game with Napoleon this afternoon. It's all arranged.' He flung himself onto his bed.

'You're actually playing chess with Napoleon Bonaparte? I can't believe it. But where? They're not going to play in the tavern are they?'

'No, no, it's going to be very grand. It'll be in the apartment of a prince. He's one of Napoleon's generals. Napoleon's valet came round today to arrange it all and Schmidt and his friends are carrying the chessmaster's cabinet over to his apartment right now. Look! Here are the invitations for you and me.' He held out two little cards, edged in gold, and Belle saw the name *Prince de Neufchatel* in beautiful curly writing.

She took the card and ran her fingers over the gold edging. 'An invitation from a prince! It'll be an awfully grand reception.'

The thought of her brother on his own in the cabinet under the gaze of everyone in that grand room, made her feel anxious for him.

'Gosh, Joe, are you feeling nervous?'

'No, not really. Maybe a little. But no one'll know that it's me in the cabinet, so I'll be OK whatever happens,' he pulled a long face, 'unless of course Schmidt and Maelzel turn nasty.'

'Well if they do we'll just do a bunk and go back to London,' said Belle. 'We know we can get back easily so there's no need to worry. But I know you'll play a good game anyway. She gave him a hug. You're a wizard at chess! Come on. Let's go downstairs and see what's going on.'

The tavern was alive with people running to and fro and shouting to each other. A line of waiters was carrying hampers of wine out to the street. There was a smell of fresh baking and Belle saw platters piled high with tasty looking cakes and pastries carried out of the kitchens to be delivered to the prince's apartment.

This entire bustle was under the frantic direction of a small man with a very high-pitched voice. 'He's the Emperor's valet,' Joe told her. 'His name's Constant. I think he's a bit nervous and he keeps shouting at everyone. We'd better keep out of his way.'

Later that afternoon as Joe and Herr Maelzel left the tavern for the prince's apartment; they passed Pieter sitting in his usual dark corner. He looked up at them half-expectantly as they walked past.

'Oh poor Pieter, he wanted to come,' said Joe.

'Ach I wouldn't take that little nuisance with me,' said Maelzel. 'Come on. They are waiting for us at the prince's apartment. The cabinet is hidden behind a curtain and we can enter the room from the side, so that you will not be observed. I expect total obedience from you, you understand? Nothing must go wrong.'

Joe nodded his head.

Belle who had come down to say goodbye and good luck to her brother had seen the expression on Pieter's face and how he looked away quickly to hide his disappointment.

A wave of anger swept over her. It's so unfair, poor Pieter, he never has any fun and he's always in trouble with that bullying old pig of a father. She looked at the gold-edged invitation in her hand. Surely Joe won't be using his invitation if he's going to creep in through a side door? Pieter can pretend to be Joe and come with me.

She was so pleased with her idea that she ran straight out of tavern and was just in time to see Joe and Herr Maelzel about to turn the corner into Ringstrasse. Flapping her hands as if in a panic, she called out, 'Joe, Joe! You've got my invitation. I need my invitation.' Joe came running back towards her, looking very confused. 'What are you talking about? I gave you your invitation.'

'No I want *your* invitation,' she hissed. 'It's for Pieter. You don't need it do you?'

Joe gave a broad grin as he understood the plan. 'That's brilliant. Gosh Pieter will be really pleased. No, you're right. I don't need it. I'll be going in by the back door, and they know me there anyway. I've been in and out several times already.' He handed the little card to her and ran back to Maelzel who was tapping his foot impatiently on the kerb.

'Sorry for taking your invitation,' he called out to Belle, 'see you later.' Belle waved to him and headed back to the tavern.

Pieter was still in his corner. She sat down beside him and talked very softly. 'You'd like to watch the game with Napoleon wouldn't you?'

Pieter shrugged. 'Nah I'm not bothered.'

'But you can watch it if you want, I've got Joe's invitation for you. We can go together and you can pretend to be Joe, because he'll be in the cabinet.'

Pieter stared at her for a moment, then the first real smile she had seen spread across his face.

'What? I'll be Joe and I'll watch the game and have a bit of a laugh at all them Frenchie's dressed up like parrots?'

'Well, you'll have to dress up a bit yourself,' said Belle. 'You can borrow some of Joe's clothes.'

'Yeah, I'll swank around in Joe's clothes.' He laughed. 'What a lark!' Then his face clouded over. 'But my Dad'll be there won't he?'

'He won't be there for the game. He'll only be helping to bring the cabinet in and out of the room, so I reckon you can find somewhere to hide when that's happening. I'll warn you when they're coming.'

'Yeah, I'm good at hiding. I'll find somewhere.' He looked at her for a moment and his eyes were open and questioning, before he shifted his glance away. 'Yeah, thanks. We're mates, ain't we?'

19

THE GAME WITH NAPOLEON

IT WAS A TRANSFORMED PIETER WHO presented his invitation at the prince's house, in Joe's military style outfit, with the smart blue jacket and gold buttons, his hair carefully brushed and silver buckles on his shoes. They were ushered into the spacious first floor living room of an apartment owned by Prince Neufchatel, Napoleon's most trusted general.

On that sunny afternoon, light poured through the tall windows at the back of the room. Belle found Pieter a place behind a pillar where he could stand without being seen by his father and she walked out onto the little balcony overlooking the grey waters of the Danube, which flowed gently by on its long journey across Europe. She watched a small branch being carried along in the flow of the river.

'So very peaceful,' she heard a soft voice behind her.

The speaker was a very pretty lady in a sea-green gown. Her thick dark curls were piled high on her head.

I just wish I could do my hair like that, thought Belle.

'Yes, Madame, it is a beautiful river,' she answered politely and curtsied. She was good at curtsies now, neatly tucking one foot behind and bobbing down briefly, keeping her back straight.

'Come now, the prince has arrived,' said the lady. 'We must return to the reception.'

The room was full of colour, noise and sparkle. All the ladies wore soft flowing gowns in pale shades, sparkling with jewels. The men were in military uniform with bright red or blue jackets, gold epaulettes and swords at their sides. Champagne in tall glasses was passed round on silver trays and there was a buzz of chatter and a feeling of anticipation in the crowd. She could see the chessmaster's cabinet now on display at the side of the room. The wooden face of the Turkish chessmaster in his robes and turban stared out at the guests, who were gathered round it, admiring the workmanship.

Poor Joe. I hope he doesn't have to wait too long in the cabinet, she thought as she went to rescue Pieter from behind his pillar.

Pieter was enjoying himself, bowing low to all ladies and helping himself to each of the trays of delicacies as they came past.

'Just look at those gents,' he whispered, pointing to a group of officers standing nearby. 'Would you believe they could squeeze themselves into them white knickerbockers?'

A large officer, with a very red face and thick side burns who made Belle think of a walrus, turned to talk to one of the ladies at his side.

'What about that one, eh?' whispered Pieter. 'He'd need a mighty big bar of soap to get him into them trousers. Oh no don't bend down, please sir.' As the officer bent over to kiss the lady's hand Pieter covered his face in mock horror. 'They're gonna split, I know it.'

Belle had tears in her eyes trying to stifle her laughter. 'Sh! Pieter,' she said. But he just grinned. 'Oh they won't hear me, don't you worry. They've all got more 'portant stuff to think about.'

The audience was beginning to move into position and Belle found a good place for the two of them, slightly hidden but with a clear view of the chessboard. She was beginning to feel uncomfortably nervous for Joe. When are they going to start?

'This will be a very interesting event,' the lady in the sea-green gown was standing beside her again. 'The automaton has an amazing reputation. It seems that through a complicated system of wheels and cogs it is actually able to think twice as fast as a man, and so be able to beat the most skillful players at chess. Now isn't that extraordinary?'

Belle felt a poke in her ribs and had to stifle a giggle as Pieter pulled an expression of mock amazement. He shook his head solemnly. 'Thinks twice as fast as a man,' he muttered, 'now would you believe it?' The French lady gave the boy a strange look and Belle replied quickly. 'Oh yes, it is indeed quite extraordinary.'

She couldn't concentrate on the chatter around her any longer. Her mouth felt dry and her stomach was churning, she was worrying so much about Joe. Napoleon's valet, Constant, was darting from group to group. Then she heard a slight noise, and saw him hurry towards the doors, which were thrown open by two footmen.

It was a surprise for Belle to see such a very small man surrounded by tall guards walk in through the door. Is that really the great Emperor Napoleon?

'His Imperial and Royal Majesty, Napoleon the First, Emperor of the French, King of Italy, and Protector of the Confederation of the Rhine,' the valet announced.

There was a sudden hush and Belle copied her neighbour as all the ladies sank into a deep curtsey and the men bowed low.

She was relieved to see Pieter bowing too, but he winked at her as he straightened up, 'His Imperial midget,' he muttered.

Napoleon walked slowly through the room, smiling at his guests and greeting one or two by name as his valet guided him to the chessmaster's cabinet.

He does look like an Emperor, thought Belle, even though he is so small. He doesn't have to make any effort. It's as though he already owns everything.

Belle felt another nudge in the ribs, 'Just look at ol' Maelzel,' Pieter whispered. 'He's bowed down so flippin' low. I don't reckon as he'll ever get up again.'

'Sh!' whispered Belle. 'You must be quiet or we'll get into real trouble.'

Napoleon was speaking. 'Ah, so I am to play a game with this magnificent contraption, am I?'

'Indeed, if that is your majesty's pleasure, I would be deeply honoured,' croaked Maelzel.

Napoleon sat down in front of the cabinet and gave a little nod to the wooden, turbaned figure opposite him.

'Come on then comrade, let's play chess. Here's to us two,' he said, laughing.

Belle's heart was beating painfully fast as she watched the mechanical chessmaster raise his hand and make a sign to the Emperor to ask him to begin. 'Good luck Joe,' she murmured. She could hardly bear to watch.

The game opened with two or three straightforward moves.

'Hey that ain't right,' muttered Pieter beside her and to Belle's surprise she saw that the Emperor had made a false move. 'He must have done that on purpose,' she whispered back. The Turkish automaton bowed its head, took up the piece and put it back in its place. Well done Joe.

'But what is the Emperor doing now?' came the voice of the lady next to her as Napoleon cheated for a second time.

This time the automaton bowed again but took the piece off the board.

'Ah that's right,' said Napoleon and then calmly cheated for the third time.

There was a pause, then a cry went up from the startled company as they watched the automaton's arm in its red silk sleeve, sweep across the chessboard, upsetting the whole game and dropping most of the pieces into the Emperor's lap.

Pieter's jaw dropped. 'Oh Gawd, what you done that for Joe? You've had it now, mate.'

There was deathly silence and the entire room seemed to be holding its breath.

Belle saw Maelzel look around frantically as if wondering how to escape.

She felt her chest tighten and for a few moments she couldn't breathe. What's going to happen?

Then with enormous relief she heard the Emperor laugh. He rose to his feet, scattering the chessmen from his lap onto the floor. 'Ha, I see your Turk has a temper!' he said turning to Maelzel. 'I congratulate you on your clever invention, Monsieur.'

A little titter of laughter went round the room as the hum of conversation started up again.

'*Bien joue*, well played Mr Automaton!' said the lady in the sea-green gown.

Bending down and holding her fan in front of her face, she whispered confidentially to Belle, 'It is a good result. Now no one can say that the Emperor Napoleon was beaten by an automaton.' She gave a little laugh. 'He may be the most powerful man in Europe, but I believe he is not a great chess player,' and dropping her voice even lower, 'it is said that he also cheats at cards!'

Belle was still too shaken to reply but she nodded her head. She was thinking of something else, something she had seen just before the chessmen were swept to the floor. She had looked up at the chessmaster's face and met, instead of the blank glassy stare of the automaton, two sparkling dark eyes. 'Ah yes, he is well known for his temper,' the Baron had said. It wasn't Joe who scattered the chessmen, of course it wasn't. It was Kadir, the spirit of the chessmaster.

Slowly the crowd, all talking to each other about that most unusual game of chess, made their way out of room.

'You'd better go,' she whispered to Pieter. 'Your father will be coming to take the cabinet out soon.' Pieter nodded gave her a grin and slipped away into the crowd.

Finally the room was empty and Joe could come out of the cabinet. He looked very pale and was wheezing badly.

Schmidt advanced on him threateningly 'So young fellow, what the blazes do you think you're playing at? Do you think you're clever, or something, insulting the Emperor?'

'Leave him alone; can't you see he needs air?' said Belle.

Schmidt turned on her. 'And you can mind your tongue as well, miss. You think you're mighty clever too, chatting away to the French ladies. What've you been telling them, I'd like to know?'

But at this point Maelzel intervened 'Let them be, Schmidt. I think it has all worked out for the best. There will be plenty of chatter about this game, and I don't think it will do our reputation any harm.'

When they had gone, Belle opened the window and helped Joe to breathe slowly. Gradually his breathing became more regular, and he no longer gasped for air.

'Joe what happened? It was Kadir, wasn't it? He came back.'

He nodded, 'I felt him there, in the cabinet, straight away, although I couldn't see him, and it felt good to have him around. I hoped he'd let me play, which he did for the first two or three moves. When Napoleon played his first illegal move, I knew it was all right to move the piece back as the chessmaster always did, but I was going to carry on the game.

'But then, when he played another illegal move, I didn't know what to do and that was when I saw that the chessmaster had taken the piece off the board, but it wasn't me who moved it.' He paused to get his breath which still sounded painful.

'Of course you knew it was Kadir who swept the pieces off the board, didn't you? I think he was angry with Napoleon for not playing seriously. I can tell you I was really terrified. I didn't know what was going to happen. But then I heard Napoleon laugh, and I just hoped it would be all right. By that time all I wanted to do was to get out of that horrible box so that I could breathe again. I don't know what happened to Kadir, I guess he just disappeared, as usual.'

He stopped talking and seemed to be concentrating hard on his breathing. Belle put her arm round his shoulders.

'I don't want to go back into that cabinet again, Belle, can we go home?'

She saw how exhausted her brother was. 'Yes, let's go back straight away. You've certainly done your bit for the Baron.'

As they left the prince's apartment, Belle recognised the young Frenchman who had approached them before. He bowed to her politely.

'That was an interesting game was it not, Mademoiselle? Tell me do you have any information for my master?'

Belle had to think quickly. 'No we have not heard anything of interest yet, but please tell your master that we are listening.'

'Thank you, I will tell him.' The young man bowed again and walked with them for a short while before turning down an alleyway. As Belle and Joe turned the corner into the square they saw Schmidt's men returning to collect the cabinet. I wonder if they saw us talking to the Frenchman, she thought, but she didn't worry about it. After all they were leaving Vienna very soon.

20

THE WAY BACK

THE SUN WAS LOW IN THE SKY AS BELLE AND Joe slipped out of the tavern and made their way back to the Schönbrunn Palace gardens.

'It'll be just like last time, remember?' said Belle. 'These woods are the way through to Tavistock Park. Just watch the trees again, and you'll see them change.'

The slender silver birch now had small green leaves on every tiny branch. Belle watched carefully as she and Joe strode into the woods, waiting for a glimpse of the London Plane trees that she knew so well. The change had been very swift last time, although of course, she reminded herself, they had been running away from the palace then, whereas now they were taking their time. All the same a prickle of anxiety was rising as she realised that nothing seemed to be changing at all. What else should they do?

'Come on, Joe, all we've got to do is to think hard about London and the shop,' she said, but the silver birch trees, swaying gently in the evening breeze, showed no sign of change. She tried to take her mind back to exactly what had happened before but found she just couldn't remember. Panic was bubbling up inside her now. The sun had sunk to a faint orange glow showing through the trees and they had walked deep in the woods. Dark shadows were gathering behind them.

'I think we should go back to the tavern and try again early tomorrow morning. Perhaps it'll be different then, and better in the daylight.' Belle tried to sound confident.

'OK, Belle, which is the way back to the gates?' asked Joe.

She realised then that she hadn't taken any notice of the paths they'd been following. They pushed their way through scratchy branches and tripped over undergrowth in the dark and she was just beginning to think that they were totally lost when Joe called out.

'Look over there. Lights, it must be the palace.' Just another short scramble through the woods and they were back in the park. 'Come on we'd better get back before they close the gates.'

They were almost at the gates when, without warning, two large figures emerged from the shadows. A heavy hand fell on Belle's neck as her arm was yanked roughly behind her back and she yelled out loud. She saw the other man grasp Joe, who kicked out wildly. The man gave an angry shout and she saw his clenched fist land hard on Joe's back.

'Think you can kick me do you, you rotten little spy? I'll show you what we do to little runts like you.' Belle knew the voice; it was one of Schmidt's drinking companions.

'What are you doing?' she screamed. 'Stop it, stop it. We are friends of Herr Schmidt.'

'Friends are you? Oh yes, fine sort of friends who spy on us and give information to the Frenchies. Nasty little brats, we seen you with your French friends, whispering and telling them all they want to hear.'

'We aren't spies. We haven't told anyone anything, I promise.'

'So what are you doing then, creeping around here in the dark, eh? Tell me that. Got an appointment with the count have you? Or is it one of his creepy lackeys? They pays you well, I bet.' He gave Belle's arm another vicious twist and she yelped with the pain.

'Come on Karl. Let's take these little traitors back to Schmidt, and see what he wants to do with 'em.'

He put his big hairy face so close to Belle's that she drew back from the disgusting smell of his breath, which was like rotten meat.

'Herr Schmidt ain't easy with spies. I can tell you that — very nasty indeed our Schmidt can be if he gets angry.'

The two men thrust the children through the gate and into a rough cart which took them back to Gasthaus Fink. The tavern was full and noisy but no one seemed to notice the frightened children, dragged in like a couple of puppies. Belle saw Pieter glance up anxiously as the door opened, but he looked away quickly and concentrated on his chessboard.

Schmidt was on his own at his usual table and it was obvious that the big man had been drinking heavily. He was slumped in his chair and his eyes were glassy. They shoved Belle and Joe roughly towards him.

'We caught these two in the Schönbrunn gardens, waiting for their contacts. They've been sneaking information 'bout us to the Frenchies.'

Schmidt gave them a nasty grin, showing his rotten teeth. His words were slurred.

'Oh 'ave you indeed, I thought as much.' He turned to his friends. 'Never trusted 'em myself... nasty, stuck-up little brats... think 'emselves too clever by half.' He jabbed a stubby red finger at Joe. 'Yeah, especially this one... he'd 'ave got a good hiding from me this afternoon. I can tell you.'

'What shall we do with 'em?' asked the one called Karl. 'Take 'em outside?' His ugly face creased with pleasure. 'Rough 'em up a bit?'

Schmidt seemed to find thinking difficult. After a long pause he said, 'Trouble is, Maelzel mightn't like it... seems like they've got connections, you see...' The next pause was so long that Belle thought he must have gone to sleep.

'So what do we do then?' asked Karl.

'Oh lock 'em in their room. We'll deal with 'em later.' Schmidt growled at Karl. 'For the Devil's sake, man, can't you leave a body to have a drink in peace?'

The two children were pushed up the two flights of narrow stairs and into their room with a curse. The door slammed and Belle heard the key turn in the lock. For a few moments she stood in the middle of the room almost too shocked to move. She could still feel the rough hands and hear the threats. Then she looked across the room at Joe who was curled up in a ball on his bed. He had his arms over his head as if still trying to protect himself from blows. Red hot anger welled up inside her. She turned and pummelled on the door with her fists. 'You stupid, smelly, fat Austrian oafs, how dare you lock us up... just wait till Herr Maelzel hears about this.'

'I don't think Herr Maelzel will help us,' Joe said softly. 'I heard him talking to Schmidt. He was leaving Vienna this evening.'

21

GOING HOME

Belle forced her mind to start working fast. *We've got to get to the Schönbrunn gardens. It's the only way back that I know, and we've got to go quickly.*

'Come on, Joe, out of the window,' she said. 'We can do it, I'm sure we can, and we're not waiting up here for those thugs to come back for us.'

Pulling up a chair, she threw open the window and looked out into the night. The pointed roofs of the Viennese houses were close together, some overlapping, and she could see that the red tiles under their window sloped down towards the flat roof of the tavern kitchens. But below the kitchen roof there was a long, sheer drop into nothing but darkness. She shook her head in despair 'Oh no, it's too far. We can't do that.'

Joe had climbed up onto the chair behind her and was breathing down her neck. Suddenly he jumped back, pulling the window closed. 'There's someone out there,' he said. 'I saw a face in the darkness. They must be keeping guard on us.'

'Hang on, I heard something,' said Belle There was a sharp ping as something hit the pane, then another and another. 'Someone's throwing pebbles, that won't be guards.' She opened the window gingerly, and gave a gasp of relief. 'It's Pieter!'

He was standing on the kitchen roof, his pale face looking up at them, beckoning them to come down. But Belle shook her head and raised her arms as if to say 'How can we, it's too steep.' Then she saw that Pieter was pointing to the far corner of the flat roof and moving his arms up and down to mime climbing like a monkey.

'He's pointing to a drain pipe.' whispered Joe. 'I can just see the top of it now. He must have climbed up onto the roof so that means that we can climb down, but we've got to slide down the tiles to the roof first.' He peered out into the darkness. 'It's a long way down, and it'll be a hard landing.'

'We'll throw our bedding down first,' said Belle. Grabbing the pillows and feather quilt from her bed, she tossed them as hard as she could out of the window. One pillow stuck on the tiles, but the rest slid perfectly onto the flat roof below.

'OK Joe? I'll go first.' Her heart was thumping as she climbed onto the windowsill and pushed herself off, not daring to look into the blackness below. The slide down the roof was faster than she had expected and she gave a yelp of pain as her knee hit the metal guttering. But then she was over, her face buried in feather bedding. Scrambling to her feet, she saw Pieter give a small wave and signal to

Joe who was on the window ledge ready to slide. He let go and, arms flailing, hurtled towards her, landing safely on the pillows.

'Wow,' he whispered. 'That wasn't too bad.'

Gingerly, they crawled over to where Pieter was standing, his finger on his lips. He pointed to the edge of the roof, which vanished into the blackness below and they watched as he pushed himself over the ledge onto the drain pipe and disappeared.

'Can you go first this time?' she whispered, and Joe followed Pieter. She could just make out the whiteness of his face as he peered up to see if she was following.

OK, now hold on tight, she said to herself and started down the pipe. It was much harder than she thought. The skirt of her long dress kept getting caught up in the metalwork and there was a sound of cloth ripping as she jumped the last few feet and fell heavily to the ground. Breathless, she picked herself up and looked round for the others.

'Who's there?' A shout rang out into the night as the kitchen door flew open and a bright triangle of light lit up the courtyard.

Belle flung herself flat onto the ground. She could taste cold mud on her lips as she pressed her head down, keeping her body absolutely still. Her heart was pounding.

'What you doing out there?' The voice called again, and she moved her head just enough to make out the figure of a man leaning out from the kitchen door, peering into the darkness. A few metres in front of her she could see the outline of Joe and Pieter, huddled into a corner of the wall. Pieter was signalling to her to stay where she was and she let her head drop down onto the earth again, willing herself to become part of the darkness.

'It's just them bleedin' cats climbing on the roof again,' came another voice from inside the kitchen. 'Come on in Karl, and shut that door, for Heaven's sake.'

As soon as the door was shut, Belle raced across to the dark corner where the two boys were waiting.

She grasped Pieter's hand in the darkness. 'Thank you,' she whispered. In the dim light she could just make out a smile on his face as he nodded his head.

'I wanted to help you, but I gotta go quick or they'll miss me and then I'll be for it. You'll be orl right now won't you? You goin' home?'

'Yes,' said Joe, 'we're going home.'

'Good luck then,' he whispered and they watched him creep off into the darkness.

'I hope he gets back OK,' said Joe. 'Poor Pieter, I wish he could come home with us.'

Belle nodded, she'd felt a lump in her throat as she watched him disappear. 'I know. He's got such a rotten life here.'

She looked out into the darkness. The door was shut and she could no longer hear voices from the kitchen. 'Come on, Joe, we've got to get going fast now. We don't know when those thugs will find our empty room and if they come after us we won't stand much of a chance.'

They set off at a run away from the tavern, through the narrow streets of the town. The thudding of her feet on the ground sounded alarmingly loud to her, but the streets were empty and no sound came from dark houses, all with shutters closed for the night. She hadn't gone far before she realised that Joe wasn't keeping up with her. She turned back and found him leaning against a wall, wheezing badly.

'I... I... can't... run... any... more,' he whispered.

'Oh Joe, I'm sorry I made you run.' As she put her arms round him, his knees seemed to give way and he slid to the ground. Panic rose inside her as she thought she heard footsteps. Schmidt's men might be right behind them. We can't wait here. Help us someone, please!

She was holding Joe against her and could feel his chest heaving as he struggled for air. Keep calm, she told herself. I must keep calm for Joe. 'Slowly, slowly, take your time, just breathe slowly,' she whispered to him as she stroked his head. 'It's all right; we'll find somewhere to rest. Schmidt's men are probably still drinking so we'll be safe for a while.'

She felt his shoulders relax and drop down slightly. 'That's better,' she said, 'just take it gently.'

There was no sound in the street now, and as her eyes got used to the darkness, she no longer saw shadows lurking in every corner. Perhaps I imagined the footsteps, she thought, but how long do we have before they come for us? We've got to get back to the palace gardens. Thank goodness Joe's breathing was settling down and he was sitting up against the wall. 'Can you walk a bit now do you think?' She felt a wave of relief as he nodded and she helped him to his feet.

They walked very slowly until they came to a little square which was bright in the moonlight. In the centre was an old broken fountain and they sat down on the stone steps and were quiet for a few minutes while Joe rested. But Belle's mind was racing. How long did they have? Then suddenly it hit her. What an idiot I am! The palace gates will be closed all night, of course they will. We can't get back into the gardens until morning! Schmidt's men will be out looking for us before then.

'Joe,' she said softly. 'We're going to have to try to get back from here. I don't know how to do it, but I think you're probably better at it than I am. Can you try to make contact with Uncle Griff? Just concentrate as hard as you can.' Joe nodded. His face looked horribly pale and tense in the moonlight. She put her arms round him and held him close.

'I want to go home, I want to go home,' she whispered, willing herself to see the London shop, but she couldn't seem to clear her mind of everything else around her; the dark houses, the sound of water dripping in the fountain, the fear of being found by Schmidt's bullies. Concentrate, concentrate, nothing else is important. She tried again to make a picture in her mind; going up to the shop door, the glow of light through the window, the little toy monkey banging his cymbals.

Then she heard Joe's shaky voice.

'I can see him, Belle, I can see the shop. Uncle Griff's there, he's at his table.'

A great choking sob of relief rose in her chest, 'Oh yes, yes, I can see him too. There he is!'

A shimmering patch of light had appeared in the square, hovering like a glass bubble in front of the fountain and in the soft haze of the bubble she could see quite clearly the front room of the shop. Uncle Griff was sitting reading the paper. Tears were rolling down her cheeks now. 'Uncle Griff, bring us back,' she begged.

She saw him look up sharply as if he'd heard something.

'Uncle Griff, Uncle Griff,' Joe's voice sounded stronger now, intense and passionate. 'We need you, please call us back.'

Uncle Griff glanced briefly at the door of the shop as if he was expecting someone to come in, but then looked away with a puzzled expression.

'We're here, we're here!' Belle called again. Then, with a sickening lurch, she felt the ground fall away beneath her. Joe's body suddenly went limp and she held on tightly to him as something hard crashed into her back, pushing her forward. Everything went black for a moment and when she opened her eyes she found herself, breathless and shaking, standing in the shop.

'Goodness me,' said Uncle Griff, 'I never heard you two come in. What have you been up to? You look quite done in.'

He was looking over Belle's shoulder. 'What's up with young Joe?'

Belle turned round. Joe looked horribly pale, with a bright red flush on each cheek. His breath was coming in great rasping gasps, his eyes looked blank and he was swaying slightly.

'Hey, watch it old chap.' Uncle Griff jumped up and caught the boy just before he fell to the ground.

22

JOE IS ILL

JOE'S FEVER RAGED AND RAGED. HE SEEMED to be burning up, and he struggled desperately to breathe.

'A severe chest infection,' the doctor said. 'There is a risk of pneumonia, I'm afraid. In normal times I'd have him taken into hospital, but they are so short-staffed that I think he would be better looked after here.'

A terrible fear gripped Belle. Joe's going die. She could think of nothing else as she sat by his bed watching him toss and turn, burning hot, in spite of the cold flannels which she kept sponging him with.

'Joe, Joe it's me, Belle,' she whispered to him, but he gave no sign of recognising her voice, only muttering words she couldn't understand and sometimes calling out loudly as if he was horribly frightened.

Janek took turns watching by the bedside. 'Is only bad dreams,' he said. 'He will forget all when he wakes.' But Belle thought of their flight from Gasthaus Fink, and wasn't so sure.

She boiled kettles of water in the room so that the steam would help to sooth Joe's rasping breathing, and she held his head while he took little sips of cold water, his head lolling from side to side, pushing the glass away from him as if it were poison.

Uncle Griff sat beside Joe's bed, talking softly to him and stroking his forehead. 'I've seen fevers like this in India,' he said. 'We just have to wait for them to burn themselves out.'

But what if they don't burn themselves out? Thought Belle. She knew Uncle Griff was trying to sound hopeful to make her feel better but day after day there was no change. Joe still struggled, wild-eyed on his bed, his skin burning hot, muttering and calling out strange words.

'Why he ask about Kadir?' said Janek. 'Is Kadir friend of his? He call out the name and also "the star".'

'I don't know,' said Belle. She felt so guilty and responsible for Joe's illness, that she couldn't bring herself to tell anyone about where they had been. She blamed herself for taking Joe into danger. Never, ever again.

They took shifts to stay with him, but Belle wouldn't leave the room and lay down on her own bed next to Joe. Exhausted, she drifted off to into a broken sleep each night.

One night she woke up and could dimly make out a figure standing over Joe's bed. She thought it was Uncle Griff but, as her eyes grew used to the dark, she recognised instead the ghostly figure of the young Turk, Kadir. A suffocating surge of panic rushed through her. He's trying to take Joe with him to the spirit world, just as Aleksy warned me.

'Leave him alone,' she screamed as she jumped out of bed and flung her arms round Joe. The figure disappeared instantly. Joe woke up slightly and muttered, 'Belle?'

'I'm here, Joe, I'm here. Don't go, please don't go.'

She spent the rest of the night on the floor next to Joe's bed and when she woke, the room was deathly quiet. With terrible certainty she felt that Joe was dead. Fear held her back for a few moments, but finally she made herself stand up. With her heart thumping she bent down over her brother. He was lying quite still and breathing softly and peacefully. She touched his forehead and found it cool against her hand. Uncle Griff was right. The fever had burnt itself out at last.

She could hear Uncle Griff coming upstairs and she called out. 'He's all right. Joe's better, he's not going to die.'

Joe opened his eyes and looked in surprise at his sister. 'Belle, where've you been? I couldn't find you,' he whispered in a croaky voice.

'You've been a long way away, Joe. You've been very ill.' Belle burst into tears.

'Come on, old girl, no need for tears now,' said Uncle Griff, 'I think your brother would like a glass of water. He's had a long journey.'

As Belle ran downstairs to the kitchen she heard a sound which made her laugh out loud. The mechanical figures who had been absolutely silent all time that Joe had been ill were now twirling and whirling, banging drums and playing their instruments. The juggler was throwing balls into the air and the soldier blew a fanfare on his trumpet. 'He's better,' she called out to them, 'but you know that don't you. Come on Meffy. I know he'd be pleased to see you.' She took the old devil up to Joe's room and set him by his bed, where he played the sweetest tune she had ever heard him play on his lute.

The doctor advised plenty of bed rest for Joe. 'He's had a bad go,' he said. 'It'll take him a while to get his strength back. Fresh fruit would be good, if you can get any. I used to suggest oranges, with plenty of vitamin C, but there haven't been any oranges since the start of the war.'

'Blackberries have vitamin C don't they?' said Belle. There are plenty of blackberries in the gardens round here.'

So a few days later she and Janek went foraging. The fine houses in Middleton Square had been abandoned, their bombed-out gardens turning quickly into jungles. Thick brambles covered the broken walls and she and Janek filled their bags with blackberries. Belle scrambled over the rubble into the corner of one of the gardens, and found a small apple tree with sweet ripe eaters ready to fall. She sank her teeth into one and the juice spurted into her mouth. Oooh! It tasted good.

From the top of the wall she looked up into the soft blue sky. The late summer sun felt warm on her back and for the first time for as long as she could remember she felt carefree, a wonderful glowing feeling that everything was going to be all right. There were no planes for as far as she could see in the sky and London had been quiet for months. Perhaps the war really is going to end.

'Look what I've found,' she called out, holding up the shiny red apples as she ran down the slope. She missed her footing and landed in a heap at the bottom, laughing and still holding the apples. Janek helped her up, joining in her laughter as she offered him one of the apples. 'Come we take these back to your brother.'

But the good feeling didn't last long.

As he pushed his plate away after the meal a few evening's later, Uncle Griff looked at her across the table. 'I'm afraid I've got a bit of a problem, old girl,' he said. Then he shook his head. 'Well, there's no two ways about it. I've been borrowing a bit of money here and there and now the blighters are calling it in. So that's it, I'm afraid.'

'Don't you have the money?' Belle heard her voice sounding small and frightened and she knew the answer before Uncle Griff replied.

'No, not enough, but don't worry, I've looked into things. The local council has a plan. They're offering to buy up bomb-damaged premises like this one. I suppose they'll be redeveloping around here after the war. They aren't offering much, but it would keep us going for a while. I could pay the blighter what I owe him and I think I could rent somewhere cheap if we moved further out of town. Maybe I could get some work if I travelled around a bit, though goodness knows it's hard enough to find anything with my blooming leg.'

'No,' whispered Belle, tears welling up. 'No, you can't sell the shop, you can't.' She stared at her uncle. I trusted him and he's let us down. What'll happen if he can't find anywhere to live? We'll be sent to one of those horrible children's homes.

The anger that boiled up inside her took her by surprise. Tears were running down her face and she heard herself shouting, hardly recognising her own voice.

'So you're doing a bunk again are you? You want to get rid of us, dump us somewhere so that you can trot off on your travels. You don't care about us, you just don't care.' The sobs were coming thick and fast now and she could hardly talk.

Through her tears she could see Uncle Griff's shocked face, staring at her. He spoke slowly and deliberately. 'I don't want to get rid of you. What can I do?' He held out his hands with the palms up, his shoulders drooped and he looked so helpless that Belle felt even angrier. Why is he so completely useless? She turned and rushed upstairs and she heard the front door slam shut as she reached her bedroom.

Joe was asleep. She lay down and put her arms round him. 'We're on our own again Joe,' she whispered, 'but don't worry I'll always, always look after you.'

He stirred in his sleep and muttered something '...find the star.'

Belle slipped into her own bed. The tears had dried up and she felt calmer now but very tired. She tried to push the mess of angry, hopeless thoughts as far as she could to the back of her mind. A picture of Uncle Griff's shocked face came back to her and she wanted to say sorry for shouting at him. It isn't his fault, she knew that. If only we could get some money. We all need a home, a proper home. Joe and I do, Janek does, even Uncle Griff does, and the shop's so right for us. She let her mind slip into her favourite daydream of families coming into the shop and a little museum where children could play with the mechanical marvels. What does Joe mean '... find the star?' She didn't know, but somehow it made her feel a bit more hopeful. She squeezed her fists tight into a ball. 'Don't give up,' she whispered.

23

AUTUMN

AUTUMN CAME ROARING IN LIKE A LION THAT year. Fierce winds ripped through the bombed-out houses, scattering loose tiles and whipping up swirls of black dust from the rubble. The heavy rain, which followed a long dry summer, found all the leaks in the shop and buckets stood in the upstairs rooms to catch the steady drips of dirty water.

Then dreadful news came from Poland. There was an uprising in Warsaw. Polish soldiers, men, women and even children, fought on the streets for nearly a month but in the end they were defeated. Many were killed and the German army took terrible revenge, burning much of the city. All this time the Russian army was lined up outside the city, under orders from their generals not to give help to the Poles.

'But the Russians are supposed to be on our side,' said Belle. 'Why are they helping the Germans?'

'Oh the Russians have got their own plans,' said Uncle Griff. 'They certainly hate the Germans but they've always wanted Poland, and I reckon they're thinking that, if Germany's finally defeated, they'll just walk into Poland when the war's over, simple as that! It's an old story.'

Belle thought of Aleksy on the road to Vienna. '*There are greedy giants on our borders who want our land.*'

'Poor Poland,' she said. 'It doesn't seem as if anyone can help them now.'

For a while Janek listened to the BBC news with Uncle Griff on his radio, but eventually he could bear it no more.

'It is over,' he said one afternoon as he shut the door and went to his room, where he stayed for the next three days.

When Belle brought in a tray of food she found him lying on his bed staring at the ceiling. Aleksy's button was on the table beside him. He turned his head away from her without saying anything and she left the tray on the floor. 'Just leave him be,' said Uncle Griff. 'We can't help him yet, but he knows we're here.'

After three days Janek came downstairs, smiling bravely at their anxious faces.

'Thank you,' he said. 'You are very kind. I think I cannot go back to Warsaw ever.' His lip trembled and he bowed his head to hide tears.

Uncle Griff stood up and put his arm round his shoulders. 'Well done, old chap. Keep your spirits up, that's the thing. You're welcome here, you know that.'

The young man shook his shoulders free and held his head up.

'I mend your house,' he said.

From then on the shop was full of the sounds of banging and sawing as Janek set about the repairs. He collected scrap timber from the bombed-out buildings, old window frames and doors, even old nails which he carefully straightened out. Some of his army mates came round to help with the heavier work.

Belle learnt how to make Polish cabbage soup and Uncle Griff found some beer for the lads. One evening they sang the song of the Polish freedom fighters.

Janek told them that the words meant. *Poland has not died, so long as we still live.* The boys sang in harmony, huddled together, their eyes staring far into the distance. It was the saddest song Belle had ever heard.

Uncle Griff gave her hand a squeeze. She looked up and saw that his face was red and he was blinking his eyes. He pulled out a handkerchief and blew his nose. 'They're good lads. I wish we could give them a home here. By golly they deserve one.'

Belle nodded and a flicker of hope lit up inside her. No more had been said about selling the shop. Janek and his friends had done a fantastic job with the repairs. She was beginning to hope against hope that it might not happen.

Then one afternoon when she got back from school, Janek was waiting for her. 'I think your uncle has some trouble.' he said. 'Two men come to ask for him today.' He screwed up his face, imitating an evil expression, 'Not good men, not friends, I think.' He shrugged his shoulders. 'I think they make threat. Is possible?'

Belle felt her chest tighten into a hard ball of fear. Uncle Griff was out nearly every evening now. Sometimes she would wait up for him and watch from her room as he came through the door, carrying a full canvas bag in each hand. She knew there were Black Market gangs on the street, selling stolen goods, but she'd never felt brave enough to ask him anything. Now he was in trouble. It was a relief to share her fears with Janek.

'I think you're right. I think he may have got mixed up with some dangerous people. But it's not for himself. He's doing it for us. You see we've got no money and he's going to have to sell the shop.'

Janek listened quietly. 'I understand. That would be bad. This shop,' he looked around with a smile, 'it has some magic. But if your uncle is with bad types he must have protection. I will help.'

Two nights later the door of the shop was flung open with a crash and Janek staggered into the room. At first Belle couldn't make out what he was dragging with him. Then everything went fuzzy and she heard herself scream as she recognised Uncle Griff's face covered in blood.

Joe rushed down the stairs His mouth open in a terrible howl as he flung himself onto the floor. 'He's dead!'

Janek put his hand on the boy's shoulder. 'No, no, not dead, they knock him out. Get water, Joe. Will be OK. Come… some cushions.'

Together they heaved him onto the carpet and put cushions under his head. As Belle bent over to wash away the blood, Uncle Griff's eyes flickered open. His voice was thick and slurred, but he managed a crooked smile. 'Don't worry, old girl. This young fellow here saved my bacon. I'm proud to have been defended by the Polish Free Army.'

Belle noticed for the first time that Janek also had a graze on his cheek. He had kept his word about protecting Uncle Griff.

After he'd allowed Belle to wash and dress his bruises and Joe had brought in a tray of tea, Uncle Griff looked round at the anxious faces and declared that he felt just fine.

Belle's heart was still thumping. 'Who hurt you, was it about the money?' She knew before he answered that it must be.

Uncle Griff rubbed the side of his face gently. 'Well, yes I couldn't come up with the money I'd borrowed, you see. The blighters wanted it back and one of them followed me home. He caught up with me at the corner of Duke Street and thumped me hard. I thought I'd had it. But then out of nowhere this young fellow,' nodding at Janek, 'appeared and went for him with a couple of damn good punches.' He chuckled. 'The blighter certainly knew he'd met his match and he scarpered, disappeared just like that.'

He raised the cup of tea he was drinking. 'A toast to my hero,' he said.

'To Janek,' said the others, raising their teacups.

Janek looked a bit embarrassed but his face was flushed with pleasure. He raised his own cup of tea and gave a rather formal little nod to each of them in turn.

'To my very dear friends,' he said, then added something in Polish.

'Is Polish saying,' he explained. 'In English, my friends tell me, you say, *May we always be there for each other.*'

Before she went to bed, Belle tiptoed into Uncle Griff's room to say goodnight. She found him sitting up in bed in his red and white striped pyjamas. The bruises on his face looked ugly but he didn't seem too uncomfortable. In his hand were the deeds of the shop that Gerard Duport had given him.

'I'm sorry about this, old girl,' he said. 'I'm going to have to take the deeds round to the council in the morning. They've offered me an advance on the shop. We're going to have to sell, I'm afraid.' He looked up at her. 'I did my best, but...' he shrugged his shoulders in an expression of defeat.

'Yes I know,' said Belle, 'I... I'm sorry.' She felt bad. Uncle Griff got into all this trouble because I pushed him into keeping the shop. But something had changed inside her. She knew now that it wasn't just the shop that was their home, it was them, all of them caring for each other, being there for each other, just as Janek had said. That's what makes a home.

She touched his arm gently. 'It's not so important, Uncle Griff. Thank goodness you're all right. I was wrong about the shop. It really doesn't matter as long as we stay together.'

Uncle Griff put his hand up to cover hers.

'I've never known how to make a home, old girl... been a ship at sea without a port for most of my life.' He looked

159

away from her, almost as if talking to himself and his voice sounded shaky.

'There are some things about your old uncle that I've never told you about. You see I went to pieces a bit... just couldn't take the war and everything.' He shook his head. 'Not proud of myself, old girl. I went on the streets and lived rough for a while. Sometimes I'd lie on the ground, looking up at the sky, just daring one of those rotten old bombs to drop on me.' He shook his head and gave a small embarrassed laugh. 'You must think I'm plum crazy, but... I don't know... I couldn't seem to make sense of anything. I was drinking too much as well, in fact I was a blinking mess.'

'So that's why you didn't come and visit us in Kent?'

'Well, I was pretty ashamed of myself... didn't think you'd want to see a barmy old uncle, and I reckoned you were happy where you were. I'd no idea how to look after children, you see... I thought I wouldn't make much of a job of it. But,' he smiled, 'it turns out we look after each other just fine.'

Belle stroked his hand. 'Yes we do, just fine.'

'Well, when my old mate Gerald did me a favour leaving me the shop I'd hoped I might make a go of it. I know this shop's a good project, and when the war's over people will want to have beautiful things again. If only we could have kept going, but... well, the money's all gone and that's that, old girl.'

'I'm sorry about all this rubbish,' he pointed to his bruised face. 'I got into a beastly mess, my own fault of course, silly nuisance, but don't worry, it won't happen again. It's the old straight and narrow from now on. You two are real troupers, and there's our young hero, Janek. We'll stick together, and we'll come through somehow.'

Belle leant over and put her head on her uncle's chest, and for the first time she felt his arms go round her. The tight knot of worry inside her started to melt away. She felt safe and cared for and to her surprise found she was crying again.

'Hey what's this, old girl?' she heard him say. 'Come on; stiff upper lip and all that.' She looked up and saw that his face was gentle.

'I love you, Uncle Griff,' she said and he didn't even try to make a joke of it.

24

THE BARON'S
LAST VISIT

WHEN JOE FIRST CAME DOWNSTAIRS AFTER
his illness, he looked as though he had been
stretched out. He was very thin, and his legs
and arms seemed to have grown several inches.
'Looks like you got yourself a pair of sticks for arms,' said
Uncle Griff. The sleeves of that sweater don't come down
below your elbows.'

Joe grinned. 'I'm nearly as tall as Belle.'

But Belle had noticed another change in him, something
about his eyes that was different. He looked as if he had been
a long, long way away and hadn't quite come back. Sometimes
he sat quite still for a long time, just staring in front of him.
She missed the little brother who used to snuggle up to her
and she wanted to hug him like she had before but somehow
it didn't feel quite as easy now. He seemed older, more separate
from her. She was sure that something was wrong.

'What is it, Joe?' She asked. 'What are you thinking about?'

He took few moments to look at her. 'What do you mean, Belle?'

'There's something wrong, isn't there? Please tell me about it. Perhaps I can help.'

'No there's nothing wrong. It's just that there's something important I've got to do and I don't know how to do it.'

How can Joe have something so important that I don't know about? He always used to tell me everything. 'Why didn't you tell me, Joe? What's this all about?'

The faraway look was in Joe's eyes again. 'It's Kadir. He keeps coming to me. He still wants something from me. I don't understand what it is, but I can tell it's really important. He was there all the time when I was ill, you see, begging me to help him. His face... Oh Belle... It is such a sad face... I've got to help him. I think he's sort of trapped, and he wants me to set him free. That's how it seems in my dreams. We're often playing chess together in an orchard and then he waves goodbye and floats up into the clouds. But he reaches out to me as if he's asking me to help him, but I don't know how to.'

Belle wanted him to stop. His words shot through her like an icy wind. There was Aleksy's warning that the spirit might try to take someone back, and the frightening memory of Kadir bending over Joe's sick bed. She blurted out. 'Don't let him take you Joe. Don't let him take you.'

Joe looked surprised, and then he laughed.

'No Belle. Don't worry that's not what it's about. It's not me he wants, it's something that I can get for him. I've been having other dreams. It's a bit like a puzzle, but I can't seem to put all the pieces together. That's what I've been thinking about.'

'Yes, yes, go on.'

'Well, there's another weird dream that still keeps coming back. It's about some men dressed in Arabian clothes talking angrily to each other. They're walking down a corridor with white walls and black and white tiles on the floor and once Kadir showed me the most beautiful sparkling star, cupped in his hands and he wanted me to take it but, when I reached out for it, it dissolved. You know Meffy and the mechanicals told us to look for the star and I think it's got something to do with that. I've been trying to work out the clue about the Arabians. I think the black and white tiles are the chessboard, and there's a special chess move that Kadir caught me out on called "Arabian mate". I can show it to you if you want.' But Belle shook her head impatiently. 'I don't need to see the move Just tell me what a chess move has got to do with the star?'

Joe shook his head. 'I don't really know but I've got a bit of an idea. I found something very strange in a box in our room. I should have told you about it before. Do you remember that first day when I unpacked one of the boxes from Philadelphia in our bedroom and found the chess set? Well the empty box is still there and when I was clearing up I found a slip of paper inside it. It must have come off the chess set. I suppose I didn't notice it on that first morning because I was so excited to find the board. I'll get it for you and you can see.' Joe ran upstairs and came down with a small brown label attached to a piece of string.

WOODEN CHESSBOARD AND MEN
late eighteenth century
(Thought to have been used by von Kempelen's famous Mechanical Turk).

Belle looked at Joe, hardly believing what she had just read. Ideas exploded in her head like rockets.

'You mean this is the Turk's board, the one that was made for the original cabinet, and you've been using it since we came to the shop?' Joe nodded. 'But that explains everything doesn't it? That must be why Kadir came here, he was looking for his chessboard. And I suppose the Baron followed him. But that's crazy Joe. How on earth did the chessboard get here? Why wasn't it burnt in the fire?'

'I don't know, but there's a note as well, to Uncle Griff from his friend Gerald. Here you are.'

Belle read out, '*To my dear friend Griff Kennedy, Hoping this finds you well. The origin of this chess set is unknown, but I was told that it is the set which was used by von Kempelen's famous Turkish chessmaster. Apparently the set had become separated from the automaton and the cabinet before they were sent to the Chinese Museum in Philadelphia where it was destroyed in a fire. This is probably a tall story, but possibly of interest to you as a chess player. It might make a good yarn after the game! Best, Gerald. . .*

'We've got to tell Uncle Griff about this. After all, the note's addressed to him. Let's have a look at the chess set now Joe, can we?' We might recognise something about it.'

Joe came back with the board and put it down on the table. He bent his head to examine it carefully and ran his fingers along the side. 'Yes there was a little scratch on the side, I remember it from when I played with Aleksy. This is the chessmaster's board. Isn't that weird? But I'm sure this isn't the one I played Napoleon on. Maelzel must have made a new board. So perhaps this one was separated when the cabinet was left in Emperor Frederick's cellars. You're right Belle, it must have been the chess set which brought Kadir here to the shop, and now for some reason he needs it back.'

As she sat looking at the chessboard, Belle suddenly knew that something in the room had changed, it felt cold and she could hear the mechanicals shuffling around.

Standing by the shelves was the tall figure of the Baron in his long grey coat. It was a very different Baron from the last time they had seen him. His face with the deep-set eyes was as intense and real as ever, but his body in the coat was so thin that it was almost transparent and the long black boots seemed to be floating slightly above the ground.

She could hear him speaking softly to himself. 'The chessboard, ah yes the chessboard, of course why didn't I think of it before? The children have the chessmaster's board. I thought it was consumed with the cabinet in the fire in Philadelphia. So that is why he comes here to this little London shop.'

Turning to the children he bowed and said. 'Bella and Jozef, I am pleased to see you again. You have done well and have done me a great service, for which I thank you but now I have one more favour to ask you.' His voice was faint and rasping and Belle thought he sounded very tired.

'Please do sit down,' she said, offering him Uncle Griff's chair, but the Baron waved it away. 'I do not have much time but I have many things to tell you. You must understand how important it is that you do this for me. You have followed me in this story of the chessmaster, but there is much you still do not know.'

His voice sounded stronger now. 'I made many interesting things in my life as a scientist and an inventor, but my real dream was always to make a machine that could think. I truly believed that it was possible. As you know, my chess-playing machine was a fake... indeed a double fake. There was the concealed human chess player but there was also the spirit of the young Turk who only you and Captain Aleksy discovered. I so wished for my machine to amaze that I trapped him in the cabinet with my magic and I promised him that I would set him free, but I was not able to keep my promise. When I left King Frederick's court and the cabinet with the chessmaster rotting in the basement I confess I forgot about him.'

'Oh,' said Belle, 'but he has been trapped for nearly 200 years!'

The Baron shrugged his shoulders.

'Time means little in the spirit world, but after all these years he is demanding that I honour my promise to him and he must be freed. His voice led me to London in 1944 to this shop and then to Jozef, who had seen an image of the young Kadir himself. I could feel that Joe was a medium but I did not know then that he was also the owner of the Turk's chessboard which I had thought was consumed in the fire. Without it Kadir cannot return to the spirit realm. It is because you have the chess set, Jozef. That is why he comes to you.'

Joe nodded. 'I guessed that, but why does he need it?'

'I can explain. Earthbound spirits have the chance to move back to the spirit world, but they sometimes attach themselves to objects that are of particular significance to them in their earthly life. Without these they fail to make full transition to the spirit realm. On earth Kadir made contact with our world through his chess set. Without the chess set he cannot be free.' The old man turned to Joe. 'You must go to Philadelphia and return it to him so that he can go back. You must make the journey for me.'

No, thought Belle, No way, we're not going back, but before she could speak Joe answered.

'I'll go,' he said, 'I'll do it for Kadir. I hate to think of him trapped here.'

Belle felt a shiver of fear as the memory of their last visit flashed into her mind. 'No,' she said. 'Neither of us can go. It's too dangerous. Last time we very nearly got stuck in Vienna.'

The Baron smiled. 'That was not a real difficulty. You would have managed the return. You only had to persevere. Jozef will always get through, he has the gift.'

Turning to Joe he said. 'I cannot come with you this time, as you see my earthly body is fading fast, but the chessboard will take you back to the Turkish chessmaster anytime you wish it to.'

Then to her surprise he bent down in front of Belle, 'Bella, little tigress, twice you have served me well and you have protected your brother with great courage. Go with him one more time. I am asking you to do this not only because it is very important for me, but because you will find something that will also be very important to you.'

What's he talking about? He was looking straight into her eyes now, and his own were deep, deep like underground caves. His voice was gentler than she had ever heard it before.

'I know what your dream is, little Bella. I understand how much it means to you and I promise you that if you make this, the last, journey you will find something that will make that dream come true.'

Belle stared back at the Baron and Aleksy's words came back to her. 'I do not think he is a bad man, but I think that he is a man who always works for himself.' The Baron badly wants Joe to take the chessboard back, but he will also help us. My dream is to keep the shop and for us all stay here together, does the Baron know that? The name 'little tigress' made her smile, but she didn't feel like a tigress now. She felt scared and she didn't want to fight anymore. 'I'm sorry, I can't agree to this,' she said firmly, 'we're not going.'

Joe turned to her with a look that she had never seen before. 'Sorry, Belle,' he said, 'but if you won't come. I'm going on my own. I have to. you see.'

Panic shot through her. Joe mustn't go on his own. 'No, wait,' she said, 'wait at least until we've told Uncle Griff. We have to tell him about his friend Gerald and the chessboard, and we could ask his advice.'

Joe nodded. 'Yes, OK, let's talk to Uncle Griff. I think he'll understand.' Looking at Belle's face he said. 'Don't be upset, please. It'll be OK, I know it will. I must go for Kadir's sake, but I have a strong feeling that it will be good for us too.'

He turned round to talk to the Baron, but the shop was empty and the Baron had disappeared as silently as he had come.

25

TELLING UNCLE GRIFF

UNCLE GRIFF APPEARED AT THE BREAKFAST table next morning in his Maharaja's dressing gown as usual.

'We've got something to show you,' said Joe, who had been waiting impatiently for his uncle to wake up. 'It's about the chessboard.' He pulled the label and the note from Gerard out of his pocket. 'Look, this is what I found. It was in the box with the chess set but we never saw it when we unpacked it.'

Uncle Griff read it carefully. 'Well I never,' he said. 'Would you believe it? Old Gerard says that the chess set belonged to von Kempelen's Mechanical Turk? That was the automaton that played chess at the court of Maria Theresa in Vienna, even played old Napoleon, apparently.'

Joe just couldn't hold back. 'Yes,' he said, 'we know all that. We were there.'

Belle reached out a hand to stop Joe saying more, but to her surprise Uncle Griff just nodded and looked at them both.

'Well I'm blowed. I wondered what you two were up to, but I never thought of that. You were actually at the court in Vienna?'

Joe couldn't stop now and he poured out all the details; the journey from Russia, the fire in the Schönbrunn Palace, the game with Napoleon.

Belle took over when he got to the bit about Schmidt and his bullies and not being able to get back through the woods. 'It was awful,' she said, 'I thought we were stuck there for ever.'

But Joe interrupted her. 'I thought about you, Uncle Griff, that's how we got back. I could see you in the shop and I called you and you brought us here.'

'Yes, yes I remember. It was the night you were ill wasn't it?' He paused. 'I thought I heard you call me and I was looking round for you. I knew something was wrong and I felt a beastly feeling of fear creeping in. I called back to you and then all of sudden there you were in front of me as though nothing had happened.'

Belle looked hard at him. 'You're like Joe aren't you Uncle Griff? You see things that other people don't see.'

Uncle Griff pushed his hair up off his forehead and a faraway look came into his eyes. 'Oh I've had some strange adventures in my time, and not all them would be considered normal by your man in the street. I never told anyone about them, mind you, didn't want to be locked up in a blooming looney asylum. But by golly, hats off to you two. What adventures eh? I must say I admire your pluck. So here you are back safe and sound, and no more excitements planned for the time being I hope. Let's all have a bit of jolly old peace and quiet shall we?'

Belle and Joe looked at each other and Belle spoke first.

'Uncle Griff, you know you told us about the spirits in India and how everyone talked to them. Well there's a spirit called Kadir who comes to the shop sometimes.'

Uncle Griff's eyes opened wide. 'Does he, by Jove? So who's he been talking to? Are you in touch with this spirit, Joe? You were talking away to someone when your fever was high.'

'It's the spirit of the Turkish chessmaster,' said Joe. 'He's a genius chess player. The Baron trapped him in the cabinet and now he wants to be free.'

A low whistle came from Uncle Griff. 'Von Kempelen, the old devil, working a double bluff. He fooled the whole of Europe for all those years. Well I never. Who else knows about this?'

'Only Captain Aleksy Worousky, who was the first to play chess in the cabinet,' said Belle, feeling a little thrill of pleasure in mentioning his name. 'He's an ancestor of Janek's.'

'Ah, Captain Worousky the Polish hero with the wooden legs. Robert-Houdin wrote about him. Did you meet him as well?'

Belle nodded. She felt a blush rising and tears pricking her eyes. Uncle Griff must have noticed because he gave her an understanding look. 'Not all adventures end happily, do they old girl? We sometimes have to leave things behind, eh?'

'You see, I've got to go back to the museum.' Joe interrupted urgently. 'Kadir keeps asking me. He needs the chessboard to set him free.'

'He needs the chessboard? Oh yes, I understand. Spirits tied to objects in this world. I've heard of that before. But we can give him back the chessboard can't we? Your Turk sounds pretty genuine to me. I think you should help him to get back to his own world.'

Belle felt like crying now. The whole conversation had gone too far. 'No,' she said, 'No. I don't want Joe to go. It's too dangerous. I don't trust the Baron. He let us down in Vienna. The risk is just too big. Joe mustn't go, Uncle Griff please don't let him go.'

'Hang on, hang on, old girl,' said Uncle Griff. 'We need a bit of time to think this through. We don't have to do anything just now, do we? Let's take our time. Belle's right Joe. When you're dealing with the spirit world nothing is sure. Spirit magic is the most dangerous. There's always a risk. But I'd like to see the chessboard again. Why don't you bring it down and we can make a plan of action?'

Joe went up to his room to fetch the board and Uncle Griff leant across to Belle. 'What's up, old girl? I can see you're in a bit of a tizz. Can you tell me about it?'

'The thing is I'm worried that Kadir wants to take Joe with him to the spirit world. He keeps asking him to go with him, and I saw him once by Joe's bed when he was ill. That's why I don't want Joe to go to Philadelphia.'

Uncle Griff nodded, his face was very serious. 'Yes I understand the danger. On the other hand it does seem a

174

good idea to give him back the chessboard, otherwise he's going to keep on coming back to pester Joe. Perhaps we can return it without Joe having to go anywhere? After all the spirit has visited you here in the shop.'

'Yes, I've thought about that too, but Joe seems so sure that we have to find the chessmaster in the museum and return it there and that's what the Baron asked us to do. But I've found that magic is always so messy. You never really know what's going on. It's like jumping into the dark. I feel frightened for Joe.'

Uncle Griff smiled 'Yes, messy is a good way to describe it. Magic has its own rules and it never tells you what they are. But we'll be careful. Let's talk it over with Joe when he comes down.' Uncle Griff went into the kitchen to make tea but after a few minutes Belle began to feel uneasy again.

'Where's Joe? Why hasn't he come down?' With a rush of panic she dashed upstairs and flung open the door of their room.

Joe was sitting on his bed clutching a paper bag which held the chessboard and chessmen. He was absolutely still and staring in front of him out of the window.

Oh no. He's going without me.

She flung herself onto the bed and grabbed her brother.

'Joe,' she shouted into the back of his jumper. 'Joe, take me with you.' The room went fuzzy for a few seconds and when it cleared she was lying on the bed still clutching Joe and his body felt warm against hers. Sunshine was streaming through the window. She felt a wonderful sense of relief. She had held onto him, he hadn't gone after all. But then she noticed that they were no longer in their bedroom. It was a different room altogether.

Stacked in the corner were what looked like stage props; a soldier's helmet and sword, two brightly coloured carnival masks, a wreath of artificial flowers. There was a large cupboard and a row of theatrical costumes hanging on a rail.

Joe turned over smiling broadly. 'Oh Belle, you came too. Thank you, thank you,' he said hugging her. 'Where are we? It looks like some kind of theatre store. Come on let's find the chessmaster in the museum. This is going to be great.'

20

THE FIRE

BELLE'S STOMACH WAS STILL CHURNING. SHE glanced around the storeroom with its collection of strange objects and then at Joe in his old-fashioned knee-length trousers and belted jacket and she felt helpless and cross. There's no point in trying to go back now. Anyway Joe wouldn't come back with me.

'OK. So what do we do now?' she asked grumpily.

'We find out what's going on of course,' said Joe as he jumped off the bed. 'Come on, Belle, I think we're in Philadelphia. Let's explore.'

The door of the room opened onto a narrow staircase leading down to the street and, turning a corner, they found themselves on the pavement outside an elegant wooden building. Above the main entrance was a sign that said *National Theater* and below it a billboard announcing that evening's performance.

Belle knew immediately where they were. 'This is where the fire started, in the theatre,' she looked around her at the busy street. 'So somewhere near here must be the museum where the chessmaster is stored.'

'Yes of course,' said Joe. 'We're here to release Kadir and that means we've got to get to the museum and give him back his chess set before the whole thing burns down and the cabinet's destroyed.' He looked around him. 'No sign of the theatre burning down yet, so I guess we're in time.'

A horse-drawn cab pulled up and a group of people in evening dress stepped out. It was a warm summer evening. The women were wearing low-necked dresses in bright coloured satins, chatting to each other about the play they were about to see. They pushed past some ragged street children playing marbles in the gutter.

'Here you,' the driver of the cab called out to Joe. 'Hold this horse for me for a dime will you?' But one of the marble-playing boys was there first. 'I'll hold him mister,' he said, pushing Joe out of the way.

'He's all yours,' grinned Joe as the boy took hold of the horse's bridle. 'Hey can you tell me where the museum is?'

The boy shrugged his shoulders. 'There's a real funny ol' place full a' junk just down that road yonder, but I ain't never been inside. Could be there I guess.'

Sure enough, a few houses down they found a faded sign:

The Chinese Museum
A collection of valuable and interesting curiosities

They pushed open the door, and a small man behind the desk who was turning the pages of a very large catalogue looked

178

up as if surprised to see them. He peered suspiciously. 'Are you visiting the museum? Tickets here please.'

I don't think he has many visitors, thought Belle, hoping that the little purse she was wearing had some money in it. Luckily she found some coins and, as the old man handed them their tickets, Joe asked 'Where can we find the Mechanical Chess-Playing Turk, please.'

'The Mechanical Turk, you say. Now, I'm not sure where they keep that ol' Turk these days. There used to be a whole lotta interest at one time. Yessir, school teachers would bring in a whole bunch of kids to see that Turk. But do you young folks know that-there chess-playing Turk was a fake? It ain't no more than an ordinary ol' conjuring trick.'

He stopped talking to swat at a fly with his rolled up catalogue and then drew closer to Joe speaking dramatically in a soft voice. 'I can tell you this, my boy. Inside that wooden cabinet there was a real life chess player stacked away behind them doors!'

Belle tried to look surprised as this was obviously what the old man expected and she was impressed by Joe's gasp of amazement.

'Yes, sure thing. That's how that whole mighty trick were done. Now would you believe that a trick like that could fool an Emperor?'

They waited for a while as the old man sat looking into the distance and shaking his head as if trying to work out this unexpected stupidity of Emperors.

After a while Belle thought she could interrupt.

'Well we would really like to see it if we may.'

'Ah well ain't nobody asked to see it for some long time. Now, let me see...' he flicked through his dog-eared catalogue. 'Ah yes,' he read slowly, 'the Mechanical Chess-Playing Turk is listed here in Exhibition Room 3, but no, that ain't right, Room 3 is bang full of Chinese porcelain now. I guess it must have been moved somewhere.'

He got up from his stool. 'Come with me. Now where would they have put him?'

Belle and Joe followed the man through rooms of strange objects. There were a few pictures and some statues and old pieces of furniture. The rooms smelled of dust and mouldy paper.

A steep winding staircase took them to a narrow corridor and that's where they found him, the world famous mechanical chessmaster, now forgotten by everyone. His red robe had faded to a dusty pink and there were jewels missing from his turban. His carved wooden face was still handsome but the dark moustache and the glass eyes were gone and the fine wood of the cabinet, which used to be polished to a deep shine, was grubby and chipped, one of the doors hanging off its hinges.

'Ah now, here he be, right here,' said the curator. 'Now you listen to this.' He took out his glasses to read the faded label.

Chess-playing automaton, originally built by Baron Wolfgang von Kempelen in 1870. The automaton travelled around Europe with various owners, and is reputed to have played chess with the Emperor Napoleon Bonaparte.

He turned round triumphantly. 'You hear that? Emperor Napoleon Bonaparte himself, and he just never guessed it were a fake. My oh my!'

'Thank you,' said Belle. 'This is just what we wanted to see. May we stay and look at it?'

'Yes, sure thing, sure thing,' muttered the old man. 'Now you make certain you open them doors to see all the machinery – it's mighty clever stuff.' and he scuttled off upstairs.

'Kadir's not here, Joe,' said Belle. 'Look at the eye sockets, they're empty.'

'Don't worry. I know he'll come. This is what he's been asking me for.' Joe seemed very sure about what he had to do and Belle watched as he took the chessboard out of the paper bag, and carefully placed it on the cabinet where it fitted into place with a loud click. Then he set up the chess pieces.

'Listen!' There was a whirring noise as if the machinery had started up of its own accord.

'He's here. Look at the eyes now!' whispered Belle.

Joe looked up. 'Kadir, I've brought the chessboard,' he said. The automaton's head bent forward slightly in a formal bow.

'What's he going to do now?' asked Belle.

'Sh! Just wait and see. I've got an idea, but I'm not sure I'm right.' The automaton's arm reached out, took away some of the pieces and re-arranged the rest on the board.

'It looks as if he's setting up an endgame,' said Joe, 'and I think I know what's going to happen next.'

'Tell me what's going on.' Belle was impatient. 'I don't understand.'

'Well, there's a checkmate pattern called "Arabian mate", it's one of the oldest moves in the game. You remember I told you I had those dreams about Arabian men walking down a corridor with black and white tiles like a chessboard? It's all fitting into place now. I think Kadir was telling me that the Arabian mate is a code for the mechanism in the cabinet. The Baron had a whole lot of tricks like that. Aleksy told me about them.'

'Look, he's moving his King now.' Joe let out a whoop of excitement as the chessmaster placed his red King on the back row and signalled to Joe to play.

'That's it, I knew it. He's set up the board for Arabian mate and it's my move. I'm going to play the winning game. Watch, Belle! My white Knight moves first to challenge the red King.'

'Check,' he whispered. The chessmaster nodded and moved his King into the corner to avoid the Knight. 'See Belle, now my white Rook moves up and the King is trapped. It's checkmate. Done it!'

'Échec, échec.' The creaking sound of the voice came from the cabinet. Then, with a loud clunking sound, the front door slid open, followed by pandemonium as everything in the cabinet seemed to be moving at the same time. Doors slid open, then shut again, cogs whirled, levers moved up and down and a cloud of dust blew out through the open door. Belle stepped back quickly. 'It's going to explode!' But just as suddenly, everything stopped.

She looked up at the chessmaster. His dark eyes were fixed on Joe's face. They were shining and bright with pleasure. Slowly and carefully he reached out both arms and lifted up the board, tipping the chessmen into his lap. He held the chessboard up for a moment then clasped it to his chest, his arms crossed in front of him.

'Goodbye, my friend,' said Joe softly, and Kadir was gone, the chessboard vanishing with him. Free again.

Just at that moment there was a shout from upstairs. 'Fire, Fire!'

'Come on, Joe. Quick, we must go back now. You've given him what he wanted. There's nothing more for us to do here.'

The curator called: 'Come up, come up here quickly. We gotta leave the building right away. The theater is afire and flames are spreading right down this street.'

'Joe, come on,' Belle pulled on his arm.

'Not yet. I need to find out what happened inside the cabinet. The code was supposed to trigger some action. It must be important, that's why Kadir wanted me to know about it. The fire isn't in the museum yet. I've got time.'

He pulled away from Belle, tied his handkerchief over his mouth and crawled into the cabinet. His muffled voice came back, 'It's a real mess in here... but something new seems to have opened up... there's a panel... right at the back... I... can... just... push... my hand in behind it.'

Belle grabbed Joe's legs, which were sticking out of the door and started to pull. 'Joe will you stop that! Don't you understand? The museum's going to burn down!' She could smell the smoke now and hear the cries of people above them. 'Leave it, Joe, leave it. There isn't time we have to get out NOW.'

There was silence. She pulled harder at his legs and heard a yell. 'Let go of me... I've found something... but I can't... quite... reach... to pull... it out...' another silence, then 'I've got it. I'm coming out.'

He was covered in dust, coughing and clutching what looked like a bundle of rags. She didn't stop to ask what it was, but dragged him up the stairs. The curator pounced on them. 'Come on outside right now. This fire is getting mighty close.'

The scene outside the museum was frightening. The fire was spreading rapidly. Thick tongues of whirling orange flames burst out of the windows of the National Theater. The air was full of smoke, the sound of cracking wood and shattering glass. The wind was driving the flames along the street and the fire was very close.

'Keep back, keep back,' shouted a policeman, as a horse-drawn fire truck came racing down the street, bells clanging, The firemen jumped out and trained their hose onto the burning buildings.

'Come on,' said Joe, holding Belle's hand tightly as they joined the crowds of people, pushing and jostling to get down the side streets and away from the fire. Belle's eyes were streaming and she could hardly see. She stumbled on a kerb stone and fell over, hitting her knee hard on the pavement. Kind people helped her to her feet, but where was Joe? She'd let go of his hand and the crowd had carried him on.

'Joe,' she called. 'Joe, come back.' She stumbled on limping, not knowing which direction to take, as the crowd split and some went one way and some another.

'Joe, Joe!' she screamed this time. 'Where are you?' Then at last she spotted him, clutching his bundle of rags and pushing back through the crowd to get to her. He waved and shouted 'Hey, Belle,' and she gulped back stinging tears.

'I thought I'd lost you.'

'It's OK,' he said. 'There's a way through here somewhere. It's quite close. I can feel it. Come on.' He pulled at her hand and she followed him, but he was going away from the crowd and back towards the fire. By this time all the houses along the street were burning. She could hear the roar of flames and the crash of falling roofs. The wind was blowing the fire towards them, showering them with sparks and the smoke was suffocating.

'No, not this way, Joe, we must get away from the fire,' she called out but he took no notice.

'There's a wall somewhere along here. I know there is. It could be this one but it looks too high for us to climb.'

Then he stopped suddenly. They had come to a gap where part of the wall seemed to have collapsed. 'Yes it's here, Belle. This is the way back, I'm sure.'

But Belle could see flames leaping up on the other side of the wall.

He's heading straight into the fire! 'No that's not right,' she shouted, but Joe was already scrambling up. She had to follow him, dragging her painful leg over the broken stones, and she'd nearly reached the top when she slipped and slithered back down the rubble, bumping and bruising herself on the way.

In front of her she could only see flickering flames, more smoke and sparks but she heard Joe's voice. 'Belle, it's OK. Come up. We'll help you.'

We? Who's we? She pushed herself up again, back over the rubble, but slipped just before she reached the top. 'No, I can't do it!' Then strong hands reached out to pull her up and over the wall. She landed heavily on the ground and groaned as the pain shot through her knee.

'Belle, you are hurt?' She heard an anxious voice.

Janek? She looked up in amazement. 'Janek, how did you get here?'

'I come to this church sometimes. They need help to repair…'

'What church?' She looked around and saw that they were indeed in a churchyard. The smoke and sparks were coming from a huge bonfire behind the gravestones.

But I know this place. It's Joe's church, St Anthony's. We're back! Relief flooded through her. She flopped down on a pile of red and gold autumn leaves and stared up at the clouds. It's all over. She felt like laughing.

Joe was looking anxiously down at her. 'Are you OK, Belle? We're just behind St Anthony's church, the one that was bombed. They're cleaning up the church yard and burning some rubbish.'

'Yes I'm fine.' Belle didn't feel like getting up from her pile of leaves now. She could see Janek peering down at her as well and they both looked so worried. The laughter kept bubbling up. She felt ridiculously happy.

Joe was still holding his bundle. 'Come on, Belle, are you OK to walk? We're nearly home. We've got to get back and tell Uncle Griff.'

27

THE SECRET

Uncle Griff was coming out of the kitchen with a tray of tea, just as they had left him.

'Hey watch out,' he cried as Joe rushed across the room.

'We did it, Uncle Griff. We did it,' shouted Joe. 'Kadir took back the chessboard, and now he's free. There was a code. It was the Arabian checkmate move. Kadir showed us.'

'There was a fire,' said Belle. They were both speaking at once now. 'The one you told us about, in Philadelphia. The museum was about to be burnt down. The poor old curator was trying to save all the things. No one was going to rescue the chessmaster, but Kadir was set free. We saw him, he looked so happy.'

'Yes, but listen,' said Joe jumping up and down in front of Uncle Griff. 'Please listen to me. The Arabian mate was a code. I knew it was and it opened a door in the cabinet.'

'Hang on, Hang on,' said Uncle Griff. 'This all sounds pretty exciting stuff, but can you both slow down a bit.' He turned to Belle. 'Why are you limping, old girl?'

'Oh I'm OK, just banged my knee.'

Janek chipped in. 'I hear Belle call out and I help her over the wall of the old church. But I think they have adventure. What happened?'

'That's just what I'd like to know. Come on, let's all sit down and you two can spill the beans, from the beginning mind you. I want to hear it all. So you found the museum, and the chessmaster? What about the fire? Did you see it? Did it really start in the theatre?'

But Joe interrupted again, putting his heavy bundle down on the table in front of him. 'Sorry, Uncle Griff. We'll tell you the whole story later. But you must look at this. It's much more important.'

'What is that? Where did you find it?' Uncle Griff didn't look very impressed.

'I keep trying to tell you. It was in the cabinet. The Arabian-mate move was a code. When I put the old chessboard back onto the cabinet it clicked in. We played the end game to chess mate and a panel at the back of the cabinet burst open.'

Uncle Griff suddenly looked much more interested. 'In the cabinet? Something hidden by old Kempelen do you think? Can we have a look?'

Belle stared at the bundle. She knew how much she'd been hoping that Joe was carrying something really special, but she almost didn't want him to open it now. What if everything that they brought back with them from a different time just disappeared, like their fine clothes always did? There might be nothing in there at all.

She thought Joe must be feeling the same, because he still hadn't unwrapped the rags.

It was Uncle Griff who reached out first and started to unpeel the dusty layers.

Then Belle heard the mechanicals start up their music and her doubts disappeared. She knew something wonderful was about to happen.

Under the layers of rags, Uncle Griff had come to a wrapping of soft black material like velvet, and Belle caught a glimpse of something shining underneath.

'I think we're nearly there. Here you are, old girl, you do the honours,' he said as he pushed it carefully over to Belle. Her heart was thumping. She half closed her eyes and pulled at the soft black cloth.

There was a louder burst of music from the shelves as the cloth fell away to reveal a beautiful sparkling object.

'The Maharaja's star!' gasped Uncle Griff. 'It is, isn't it? By Jove. How on earth did it get there?'

Two points of the star had broken off and were lying on the cloth. Some of the little stones had fallen out, but it was, without any doubt, the star they had seen in James Cox's exhibition.

'It's ours now, the star's ours. The Baron gave it to us.' Joe's face was red and he was banging his fist on the table with excitement, hardly able to get his words out.

'But how did the Baron get hold of it? The last I heard of the star it was in James Cox's catalogue.'

'King Frederick bought it from the exhibition and then he gave it to the Baron in exchange for the Turkish chessmaster, and he hid it behind a trick panel, but the cabinet was left in a cellar and he never got it back.' Joe was speaking so fast he was out of breath.

'Herr Maelzel and Schmidt tried to find it,' Belle carried on, 'but they didn't have the original chessboard, and they didn't know the code. It was brilliant Joe who worked it out.'

'Well it was Kadir who showed me,' said Joe. 'The spirits in the mechanicals knew where it was as well, but they couldn't tell us.'

'Well I never, If only old Gerald could have seen this.' Uncle Griff carefully blew some of the dust off the ornament and felt under the base for a key.

'It's a bit stiff of course… but, hang on… yes here we go. My goodness, what amazing workmanship, after all these years!'

The first circle of stars had opened up, followed by a second circle and then a third and more and more, getting smaller and smaller, as the points of the stars moved round in opposite directions, passing each other and sending a shower of glittering reflections onto the walls and ceilings.

'Three thousand precious stones,' whispered Uncle Griff, 'that's what it said in the catalogue, three thousand blooming sparklers.'

'It's worth a lot isn't it?' asked Joe.

'It's worth a fortune,' said Uncle Griff.

'We won't have to sell the shop now will we?'

'Not unless we decide to move to a whacking great mansion,' said Uncle Griff with a grin.

'I don't want to move anywhere,' said Belle, 'I want us to stay here, all of us.' Her voice went a bit wobbly. 'This is our home. We've all worked hard to make it and now we can keep it.'

Uncle Griff was smiling at her and nodding his head. She knew he would never sell the shop now.

'But I reckon we could buy one of the bombed-out sites round the corner if we were feeling a bit cramped and wanted to expand?'

'That's a terrific idea,' said Belle. We could have a mechanical toy museum for children to visit, That was my dream!'

'And I could have a decent workshop. I reckon that was my dream,' said Uncle Griff.

'Could old Zeb have a shop for his books? He's always wanted a shop because he gets so cold on the market stall. I think that would be his dream.' said Joe. 'What about you Janek?'

Janek shrugged his shoulders. He looked a bit embarrassed.

'What about setting up a little carpentry business here with your mates?' said Uncle Griff. 'You're a fine craftsman and there'll be lots to be done when the war's over and everyone's rebuilding.'

Janek's face broke into a smile. 'I can stay with you?'

'Yes of course you're staying, old chap,' said Uncle Griff. 'Where would we be without you?'

Janek bent his head and muttered a thank you. Belle saw that he had taken Aleksy's gold button out of his pocket and was twisting it in his fingers.

The sparkling star was still turning, reflecting the golden light of the autumn sunset onto the four faces round the table.

'May we always be there for each other.' whispered Belle.

POST SCRIPT

THE CHESSMASTER'S SECRET;
FACT OR FICTION?

THE STORY OF BELLE AND JOE AND UNCLE Griff has of course been made up, but it is based on a series of events which actually happened. The Turkish Chessmaster did exist!

Here are the real people behind the story:-

*The Mechanical Chess-playing Turk was created in 1770 by Baron von Kempelen while he was employed at the court of Empress Maria Theresa of Austria. Automata had become very popular by that time and the fact that the Mechanical Turk was a hoax, with a chess player hidden in the cabinet, was not recognised for over a hundred years.

*The French magician, Jean Robert-Houdin, wrote in his memoirs in 1858 about a Polish officer Captain Worousky, who, having lost his legs in a battle against the Russian army, was rescued by Dr. Orloff (a friend of Von Kempelen's) and smuggled out of Russia, hiding in The Turk's cabinet. Captain Worousky subsequently played (and won) many games of chess, playing inside the cabinet.

*James Cox (1783-1800) made wonderful mechanical clocks and automata, which he sold mainly to China and India. When changes in the tax laws made this market unprofitable, he held a grand exhibition in Spring Gardens, London, which was the talk of the town. Sadly Cox went bankrupt and many of the beautiful objects were lost. A newspaper account of May 1782 mentions 'a boy with a pine-apple on is head which opens and discovers a nest of birds' and 'a mechanical star decorated with 3000 precious stones.'

*King Frederick II of Prussia (Frederick the Great) is reputed to have bought the Turkish Chessmaster from Baron Von Kempelen for a large sum of money in order to find out how it worked. After he discovered the hoax it is said that The Turk was left to rot in the King's cellars for several years.

* Baron Von Kempelen died in 1804. His gravestone in Vienna bore the inscription. '*Non omnis moriar*' (I do not die completely).

*In 1804 The Turk was bought by Johann Maelzel who restored it and exhibited in many European countries before taking it to America.

*In 1809 Maelzel set up a game of chess with the Emperor Napoleon Bonaparte in Vienna. There are several versions of this game but the most plausible seems to be the one written in the diary of Napoleon's valet, Louis-Constant Wairy, who was present at the event. The game, as I have described it in *The Chessmaster's Secret*, is taken from Louis-Constant's account.

*In 1840 The Turk was donated to *The Chinese Museum* in Philadelphia. In July 1854 a fire broke out in the museum and The Turk was destroyed.